Classics.

# Grimm's
# Fairy
# Tales

*Abbey Classics*

© **Brown Watson** (Leicester) Ltd.

# Hansel and Grethel

Near a great forest there lived a poor woodcutter and his wife, and his two children; the boy's name was Hansel and the girl's Grethel. They had very little to bite or to sup, and once, when there was great dearth in the land, the man could not even gain the daily bread. As he lay in bed one night thinking of this, and turning and tossing, he sighed heavily, and said to his wife,

"What will become of us? We cannot even feed our children; there is nothing left for ourselves."

"I will tell you what, husband," answered the wife. "We will take the children early in the morning into the forest, where it is thickest; we will make them a fire, and we will give each of them a piece of bread, then we will go to our work and leave them alone; they will never find the way home again, and we shall be quit of them."

"No, wife," said the man. "I cannot do that. I cannot find in my heart to take my children into the forest and to leave them there alone; the wild animals would soon come and devour them."

"O you fool," said she, "then we will all four starve; you had better get the coffins ready," and she left him no peace until he consented.

"But I really pity the poor children," said the man.

The two children had not been able to sleep for hunger, and had heard what their step-mother had said to their father. Grethel wept bitterly, and said to Hansel,

"It is all over with us."

"Do be quiet, Grethel," said Hansel, "and do not fret. I will manage something." And when the parents had gone to sleep he got up, put on his little coat, opened the back door, and slipped out. The moon was shining brightly, and the white flints that lay in front of the house glistened like pieces of silver. Hansel stooped and filled the little pocket of his coat as full as it would hold. Then he went back again, and said to Grethel,

"Be easy, dear little sister, and go to sleep quietly; God will not forsake us," and laid himself down again in his bed.

When the day was breaking, and before the sun had risen, the wife came and awakened the two children, saying,

"Get up, you lazy bones. We are going into the forest to cut wood."

Then she gave each of them a piece of bread, and said,

"That is for dinner, and you must not eat it before then, for you will get no more."

Grethel carried the bread under her apron, for Hansel had his

4

pockets full of the flints. Then they set off all together on their way to the forest. When they had gone a little way Hansel stood still and looked back towards the house, and this he did again and again, till his father said to him,

"Hansel, what are you looking at? Take care not to forget your legs."

"O father," said Hansel, "I am looking at my little white kitten, who is sitting up on the roof to bid me good-bye."

"You young fool," said the woman, "that is not your kitten, but the sunshine on the chimney pot."

Of course Hansel had not been looking at his kitten, but had been taking every now and then a flint from his pocket and dropping it on the road.

When they reached the middle of the forest the father told the children to collect wood to make a fire to keep them warm; and Hansel and Grethel gathered brushwood enough for a little mountain; and it was set on fire, and when the flame was burning quite high the wife said,

"Now lie down by the fire and rest yourselves, you children, and we will go and cut wood; and when we are ready we will come and fetch you."

So Hansel and Grethel sat by the fire, and at noon they each ate their pieces of bread. They thought their father was in the wood all the time, as they seemed to hear the strokes of the axe: but really it was only a dry branch hanging to a withered tree that the wind moved to and fro. So when they had stayed there a long time their eyelids closed with weariness, and they fell fast asleep. When at last they woke it was night, and Grethel began to cry, and said,

"How shall we ever get out of this wood?" But Hansel comforted her, saying,

"Wait a little while longer, until the moon rises, and then we can easily find the way home."

And when the full moon got up Hansel took his little sister by the hand, and followed the way where the flint stones shone like silver, and showed them the road. They walked on the whole night through, and at the break of day they came to their father's house. They knocked at the door, and when the wife opened it and saw that it was Hansel and Grethel she said,

"You naughty children, why did you sleep so long in the wood? We thought you were never coming home again!"

But the father was glad, for it had gone to his heart to leave them both in the woods alone.

Not very long after that there was again great scarcity in those parts, and the children heard their mother say at night in bed to their father,

"Everything is finished up; we have only half a loaf, and after that the tale comes to an end. The children must be off; we will take them farther into the wood this time, so that they shall not be able to find the way back again; there is no other way to manage."

The man felt sad at heart, and he thought,

"It would be better to share one's last morsel with one's children."

But the wife would listen to nothing that he said, but scolded and reproached him. He who says A must say B too, and when a man has given in once he has to do it a second time.

But the children were not asleep, and had heard all the talk.

When the parents had gone to sleep Hansel got up to go out and get more flint stones, as he did before, but the wife had locked the door, and Hansel could not get out; but he comforted his little sister, and said,

"Don't cry, Grethel, and go to sleep quietly, and God will help us."

Early the next morning the wife came and pulled the children out of bed. She gave them each a little piece of bread—less than before; and on the way to the wood Hansel crumbled the bread in his pocket, and often stopped to throw a crumb on the ground.

"Hansel, what are you stopping behind and staring for?" said the father

"I am looking at my little pigeon sitting on the roof to say good-bye to me," answered Hansel.

"You fool," said the wife, "that is no pigeon, but the morning sun shining on the chimney pots."

Hansel went on as before, and strewed bread crumbs all along the road.

The woman led the children far into the wood, where they had never been before in all their lives. And again there was a large fire made, and the mother said,

"Sit still there, you children, and when you are tired you can go to sleep; we are going into the forest to cut wood, and in the evening, when we are ready to go home we will come and fetch you."

So when noon came Grethel shared her bread with Hansel, who had strewed his along the road. Then they went to sleep, and the evening passed, and no one came for the poor children.

When they awoke it was dark night, and Hansel comforted his little sister, and said,

"Wait a little, Grethel, until the moon gets up, then we shall be able to see our way home by the crumbs of bread that I have scattered along it."

So when the moon rose they got up, but they could find no crumbs of bread, for the birds of the woods and of the fields had come and picked them up. Hansel thought they might find the way all the same, but they could not. They went on all that night, and the next day from the morning until the evening, but they could not find the way out of the wood, and they were very hungry, for they had nothing to eat but the few berries they could pick up. And when they were so tired that they could no longer drag themselves along, they lay down under a tree and fell asleep.

It was now the third morning since they had left their father's house. They were always trying to get back to it, but instead of that they only found themselves farther in the wood, and if help had not soon come they would have been starved. About noon they saw a pretty snow-white bird sitting on a bough, and singing so sweetly that they stopped to listen. And when he had finished the bird spread his wings and flew before them, and they followed after him until they came to a little house, and the bird perched on the roof, and when they came nearer they saw that the house was built of bread, and roofed with cakes; and the window was of transparent sugar.

"We will have some of this," said Hansel, "and make a fine meal. I will eat a piece of the roof, Grethel, and you can have some of the window—that will taste sweet."

So Hansel reached up and broke off a bit of the roof, just to see how it tasted, and Grethel stood by the window and gnawed at it. Then they heard a thin voice call out from inside,

"Nibble, nibble, like a mouse,
  Who is nibbling at my house?"

And the children answered,

"Never mind,
  It is the wind."

And they went on eating, never disturbing themselves. Hansel, who found that the roof tasted very nice, took down a great piece of it, and Grethel pulled out a large round windowpane, and sat her down and began upon it. Then the door opened, and an aged woman came out, leaning upon a crutch. Hansel and Grethel felt very frightened, and let fall what they had in their hands. The old woman, however, nodded her head, and said,

"Ah, my dear children, how come you here? You must come indoors and stay with me, you will be no trouble."

So she took them each by the hand, and led them into her little house. And there they found a good meal laid out, of milk and pancakes, with sugar, apples, and nuts. After that she showed them two little white beds, and Hansel and Grethel laid themselves down on them, and thought they were in heaven.

The old woman, although her behaviour was so kind, was a wicked witch, who lay in wait for children, and had built the little house on purpose to entice them. When they were once

9

inside she used to kill them, cook them, and eat them, and then it was a feast-day with her. The witch's eyes were red, and she could not see very far, but she had a keen scent, like the beasts, and knew very well when human creatures were near. When she knew that Hansel and Grethel were coming, she gave a spiteful laugh, and said triumphantly,

"I have them, and they shall not escape me!"

Early in the morning, before the children were awake, she got up to look at them, and as they lay sleeping so peacefully with round rosy cheeks, she said to herself,

"What a fine feast I shall have!"

Then she grasped Hansel with her withered hand, and led him into a little stable, and shut him up behind a grating; and call and scream as he might, it was no good. Then she went back to Grethel and shook her, crying,

"Get up, lazy bones; fetch water, and cook something nice for your brother. He is outside in the stable, and must be fattened up. And when he is fat enough I will eat him."

Grethel began to weep bitterly, but it was of no use, she had to do what the wicked witch bade her.

And so the best kind of victuals was cooked for poor Hansel, while Grethel got nothing but crab-shells. Each morning the old woman visited the little stable, and cried,

"Hansel, stretch out your finger, that I may tell if you will soon be fat enough."

Hansel, however, used to hold out a little bone, and the old woman, who had weak eyes, could not see what it was, and supposing it to be Hansel's finger, wondered very much that it was not getting fatter. When four weeks had passed and Hansel seemed to remain so thin, she lost patience and could wait no longer.

"Now then, Grethel," cried she to the little girl; "be quick and draw water; be Hansel fat or be he lean, to-morrow I must kill and cook him."

Oh, what a grief for the poor little sister to have to fetch water, and how the tears flowed down over her cheeks!

"Dear God, pray help us!" cried she. "If we had been devoured by wild beasts in the wood, at least we should have died together."

"Spare me your lamentations," said the old woman. "They are of no avail."

Early next morning Grethel had to get up, make the fire, and fill the kettle.

"First we will do the baking," said the old woman. "I have heated the oven already, and kneaded the dough."

She pushed poor Grethel towards the oven, out of which the flames were already shining.

"Creep in," said the witch, "and see if it is properly hot so that the bread may be baked."

And Grethel once in, she meant to shut the door upon her and let her be baked, and then she would have eaten her. But Grethel perceived her intention, and said,

"I don't know how to do it: how shall I get in?"

"Stupid goose," said the old woman, "the opening is big enough, do you see? I could get in myself!" and she stooped down and put her head in the oven's mouth. Then Grethel gave her a push, so that she went in farther, and she shut the iron door upon her, and put up the bar. Oh how frightfully she

11

howled! But Grethel ran away, and left the wicked witch to burn miserably. Grethel went straight to Hansel, opened the stable-door and cried,

"Hansel, we are free! The old witch is dead!"

Then out flew Hansel like a bird from its cage as soon as the door is opened. How rejoiced they both were! How they fell each on the other's neck and danced about, and kissed each other! And as they had nothing more to fear they went over all the old witch's house, and in every corner there stood chests of pearls and precious stones.

"This is something better than flint stones," said Hansel, as he filled his pockets, and Grethel, thinking she also would like to carry something home with her, filled her apron full.

"Now, away we go," said Hansel; "if we only can get out of the witch's wood."

When they had journeyed a few hours they came to a great piece of water.

"We can never get across this," said Hansel, "I see no stepping-stones and no bridge."

"And there is no boat either," said Grethel; "but here comes a white duck; if I ask her she will help us over." So she cried,

"Duck, duck, here we stand,
  Hansel and Grethel, on the land,
  Stepping-stones and bridge we lack,
  Carry us over on your nice white back."

And the duck came accordingly, and Hansel got upon her and told his sister to come too.

"No," answered Grethel, "that would be too hard upon the duck; we can go separately, one after the other."

And that was how it was managed, and after that they went on happily, until they came to the wood, and the way grew more and more familiar, till at last they saw in the distance their father's house. Then they ran till they came up to it, rushed in at the door, and fell on their father's neck. The man had not had a quiet hour since he left his children in the wood; but his wife was dead. And when Grethel opened her apron the pearls and precious stones were scattered all over the room, and Hansel took one handful after another out of his pocket. Then was all care at an end, and they lived in great joy together.

Sing every one,
My story is done,
And look! round the house
There runs a little mouse,
He that can catch her before she scampers in,
May make himself a very very large fur-cap
                          out of her skin.

# The Elves

There was once a shoemaker, who, through no fault of his own, became so poor that at last he had nothing left but just enough leather to make one pair of shoes. He cut out the shoes at night, so as to set to work upon them next morning; and as he had a good conscience, he laid himself quietly down in his bed, committed himself to heaven, and fell asleep. In the morning, after he had said his prayers, and was going to get to work, he found the pair of shoes made and finished, and standing on his table. He was very much astonished, and could not tell what to think, and he took the shoes in his hand to examine them more nearly; and they were so well made that every stitch was in its right place, just as if they had come from the hand of a master-workman.

Soon after a purchaser entered, and as the shoes fitted him very well, he gave more than the usual price for them, so that the shoemaker had enough money to buy leather for two more pairs of shoes. He cut them out at night, and intended to set to work the next morning with fresh spirit; but that was not to be, for when he got up they were already finished, and a customer even was not lacking, who gave him so much money that he was able to buy leather enough for four new pairs. Early next morning he found the four pairs also finished, and so it always happened; whatever he cut out in the evening was worked up by the morning, so that he was soon in the way of making a good living, and in the end became very well to do.

One night, not long before Christmas, when the shoemaker had finished cutting out, and before he went to bed, he said to his wife,

"How would it be if we were to sit up to-night and see who it is that does us this service?"

His wife agreed, and set a light to burn. Then they both hid in a corner of the room, behind some coats that were hanging up, and then they began to watch. As soon as it was midnight they saw come in two neatly-formed naked little men, who seated themselves before the shoemaker's table, and took up the work that was already prepared, and began to stitch, to pierce, and to hammer so cleverly and quickly with their little fingers that the shoemaker's eyes could scarcely follow them, so full of wonder was he. And they never left off until everything was finished and was standing ready on the table, and then they jumped up and ran off.

The next morning the shoemaker's wife said to her husband, "Those little men have made us rich, and we ought to show ourselves grateful. With all their running about, and having nothing to cover them, they must be very cold. I'll tell you what; I will make little shirts, coats, waistcoats, and breeches for them, and knit each of them a pair of stockings, and you shall make each of them a pair of shoes."

The husband consented willingly, and at night, when everything was finished, they laid the gifts together on the table, instead of the cut-out work, and placed themselves so that they could observe how the little men would behave. When midnight came, they rushed in, ready to set to work, but when they found, instead of pieces of prepared leather, the neat little garments put ready for them, they stood a moment in surprise, and then they testified the greatest delight. With the greatest swiftness they took up the pretty garments and slipped them on, singing,

"What spruce and dandy boys are we!
No longer cobblers we will be."

Then they hopped and danced about, jumping over the chairs and tables, and at last they danced out at the door.

From that time they were never seen again; but it always went well with the shoemaker as long as he lived, and whatever he took in hand prospered.

# Mother Hulda

A widow had two daughters; one was pretty and industrious, the other was ugly and lazy. And as the ugly one was her own daughter, she loved her much the best, and the pretty one was made to do all the work, and be the drudge of the house. Every day the poor girl had to sit by a well on the high road and spin until her fingers bled. Now it happened once that as the spindle was bloody, she dipped it into the well to wash it; but it slipped out of her hand and fell in. Then she began to cry, and ran to her step-mother, and told her of her misfortune; and her step-mother scolded her without mercy, and said in her rage,

"As you have let the spindle fall in, you must go and fetch it out again!"

Then the girl went back again to the well, not knowing what to do, and in the despair of her heart she jumped down into the well the same way the spindle had gone. After that she knew nothing; and when she came to herself she was in a beautiful meadow, and the sun was shining on the flowers that grew round her. And she walked on through the meadow until she came to a baker's oven that was full of bread; and the bread called out to her,

"Oh, take me out, take me out, or I shall burn; I am baked enough already!"

Then she drew near, and with the baker's peel she took out all the loaves one after the other. And she went farther on till she came to a tree weighed down with apples, and it called out to her,

"Oh, shake me, shake me, we apples are all of us ripe!"

Then she shook the tree until the apples fell like rain, and she shook until there were no more to fall; and when she had gathered them together in a heap, she went on farther. At last she came to a little house, and an old woman was peeping out of it, but she had such great teeth that the girl was terrified and about to run away, only the old woman called her back.

"What are you afraid of, my dear child? Come and live with me, and if you do the house-work well and orderly, things shall go well with you. You must take great pains to make my bed well, and shake it up thoroughly, so that the feathers fly about, and then in the world it snows, for I am Mother Hulda." *

As the old woman spoke so kindly, the girl took courage, consented, and went to her work. She did everything to the old woman's satisfaction, and shook the bed with such a will that the feathers flew about like snow-flakes: and so she led a,

* In Hesse, when it snows, they say, "Mother Hulda is making her bed."

18

good life, had never a cross word, but boiled and roasted meat every day. When she had lived a long time with Mother Hulda, she began to feel sad, not knowing herself what ailed her; at last she began to think she must be home-sick; and although she was a thousand times better off than at home where she was, yet she had a great longing to go home. At last she said to her mistress,

"I am home-sick, and although I am very well off here, I cannot stay any longer; I must go back to my own home."

Mother Hulda answered,

"It pleases me well that you should wish to go home, and, as you have served me faithfully, I will undertake to send you there!"

She took her by the hand and led her to a large door standing open, and as she was passing through it there fell upon her a heavy shower of gold, and the gold hung all about her, so that she was covered with it.

"All this is yours, because you have been so industrious," said Mother Hulda; and, besides that, she returned to her her spindle, the very same that she had dropped in the well. And then the door was shut again, and the girl found herself back again in the world, not far from her mother's house; and as she passed through the yard the cock stood on the top of the well and cried,

"Cock-a-doodle doo!
  Our golden girl has come home too!"

Then she went in to her mother, and as she had returned covered with gold she was well received.

So the girl related all her history, and what had happened to her, and when the mother heard how she came to have such great riches she began to wish that her ugly and idle daughter might have the same good fortune. So she sent her to sit by the well and spin; and in order to make her spindle bloody she put her hand into the thorn hedge. Then she threw the spindle into the well, and jumped in herself. She found herself, like her sister, in the beautiful meadow, and followed the same path, and when she came to the baker's oven, the bread cried out,

"Oh, take me out, take me out, or I shall burn; I am quite done already!"

But the lazy-bones answered,

"I have no desire to black my hands," and went on farther. Soon she came to the apple-tree, who called out,

"Oh, shake me, shake me, we apples are all of us ripe!"

But the lazy-bones answered,

"That is all very fine; suppose one of you should fall on my head," and went on farther. When she came to Mother Hulda's house she did not feel afraid, as she knew beforehand of her great teeth, and entered into her service at once. The first day she put her hand well to the work, and was industrious, and did everything Mother Hulda bade her, because of the gold she expected; but the second day she began to be idle, and the third day still more so, so that she would not get up in the morning. Neither did she make Mother Hulda's bed as it ought to have been made, and did not shake it for the feathers to fly about. So that Mother Hulda soon grew tired of her, and gave her warning, at which the lazy thing was well pleased, and thought that now the shower of gold was coming; so Mother

Hulda led her to the door, and as she stood in the doorway, instead of the shower of gold a great kettle full of pitch was emptied over her.

"That is the reward for your service," said Mother Hulda, and shut the door. So the lazy girl came home all covered with pitch, and the cock on the top of the well seeing her, cried,

"Cock-a-doodle doo!
  Our dirty girl has come home too!"

And the pitch remained sticking to her fast, and never, as long as she lived, could it be got off.

# The Sleeping
# Beauty

In times past there lived a king and queen, who said to each
other every day of their lives, "Would that we had a child!"
and yet they had none. But it happened once that when the
queen was bathing, there came a frog out of the water, and he
squatted on the ground, and said to her,

"Thy wish shall be fulfilled; before a year has gone by, thou
shalt bring a daughter into the world."

And as the frog foretold, so it happened; and the queen bore
a daughter so beautiful that the king could not contain himself
for joy, and he ordained a great feast. Not only did he bid to it
his relations, friends, and acquaintances, but also the wise
women, that they might be kind and favourable to the child.
There were thirteen of them in his kingdom, but as he had only
provided twelve golden plates for them to eat from, one of them
had to be left out. However, the feast was celebrated with all

splendour; and as it drew to an end, the wise women stood forward to present to the child their wonderful gifts: one bestowed virtue, one beauty, a third riches, and so on, whatever there is in the world to wish for. And when eleven of them had said their say, in came the uninvited thirteenth, burning to revenge herself, and without greeting or respect, she cried with a loud voice,

"In the fifteenth year of her age the princess shall prick herself with a spindle and shall fall down dead."

And without speaking one more word she turned away and left the hall. Every one was terrified at her saying, when the twelfth came forward, for she had not yet bestowed her gift, and though she could not do away with the evil prophecy, yet she could soften it, so she said,

"The princess shall not die, but fall into a deep sleep for a hundred years."

Now the king, being desirous of saving his child even from this misfortune, gave commandment that all the spindles in his kingdom should be burnt up.

The maiden grew up, adorned with all the gifts of the wise women; and she was so lovely, modest, sweet, and kind and clever, that no one who saw her could help loving her.

It happened one day, she being already fifteen years old, that the king and queen rode abroad, and the maiden was left behind alone in the castle. She wandered about into all the nooks and corners, and into all the chambers and parlours, as the fancy took her, till at last she came to an old tower. She climbed the narrow winding stair which led to a little door, with a rusty key sticking out of the lock; she turned the key, and the door opened, and there in the little room sat an old woman with a spindle, diligently spinning her flax.

"Good day, mother," said the princess, "what are you doing?"

"I am spinning," answered the old woman, nodding her head.

"What thing is that that twists round so briskly?" asked the maiden, and taking the spindle into her hand she began to spin; but no sooner had she touched it than the evil prophecy was fulfilled, and she pricked her finger with it. In that very moment she fell back upon the bed that stood there, and lay in a deep sleep. And this sleep fell upon the whole castle; the king and queen, who had returned and were in the great hall, fell fast asleep, and with them the whole court. The horses in their stalls, and dogs in the yard, the pigeons on the roof, the flies on the wall, the very fire that flickered on the hearth, became still, and slept like the rest; and the meat on the spit ceased roasting, and the cook, who was going to pull the scullion's hair for some mistake he had made, let him go, and went to sleep. And the wind ceased, and not a leaf fell from the trees about the castle.

Then round about that place there grew a hedge of thorns thicker every year, until at last the whole castle was hidden from view, and nothing of it could be seen but the vane on the roof. And a rumour went abroad in all that country of the beautiful sleeping Rosamond, for so was the princess called; and from time to time many kings' sons came and tried to force their way through the hedge; but it was impossible for them to do so, for the thorns held fast together like strong hands, and the young men were caught by them, and not being able to get free, there died a lamentable death.

Many a long year afterwards there came a king's son into that country, and heard an old man tell how there should be a castle standing behind the hedge of thorns, and that there a beautiful enchanted princess named Rosamond had slept for a hundred years, and with her the king and queen, and the whole court. The old man had been told by his grandfather that many kings' sons had sought to pass the thorn-hedge, but had been caught and pierced by the thorns, and had died a miserable death. Then said the young man, "Nevertheless, I do not fear to try; I shall win through and see the lovely Rosamond." The good old man tried to dissuade him, but he would not listen to his words.

For now the hundred years were at an end, and the day had come when Rosamond should be awakened. When the prince drew near the hedge of thorns, it was changed into a hedge of beautiful large flowers, which parted and bent aside to let him pass, and then closed behind him in a thick hedge. When he reached the castle-yard, he saw the horses and brindled hunting-dogs lying asleep, and on the roof the pigeons were sitting with their heads under their wings. And when he came indoors, the flies on the wall were asleep, the cook in the kitchen had his hand uplifted to strike the scullion, and the kitchen-maid had the black fowl on her lap ready to pluck. Then he mounted higher, and saw in the hall the whole court lying asleep, and above them, on their thrones, slept the king and the queen. And still he went farther, and all was so quiet that he could hear his own breathing; and at last he came to the tower, and went

25

up the winding stair, and opened the door of the little room where Rosamond lay. And when he saw her looking so lovely in her sleep, he could not turn away his eyes; and presently he stooped and kissed her, and she awaked, and opened her eyes, and looked very kindly on him. And she rose, and they went forth together, and the king and the queen and the whole court waked up, and gazed on each other with great eyes of wonderment. And the horses in the yard got up and shook themselves, the hounds sprang up and wagged their tails, the pigeons on the roof drew their heads from under their wings, looked round, and flew into the field, the flies on the wall crept on a little farther, the kitchen fire leapt up and blazed and cooked the meat, the joint on the spit began to roast, the cook gave the scullion such a box on the ear that he roared out, and the maid went on plucking the fowl.

Then the wedding of the Prince and Rosamond was held with all splendour, and they lived very happily together until their lives' end.

# Snow-white

It was the middle of winter, and the snowflakes were falling
like feathers from the sky, and a queen sat at her window working, and her embroidery-frame was of ebony. And as she
worked, gazing at times out on the snow, she pricked her finger,
and there fell from it three drops of blood on the snow. And
when she saw how bright and red it looked, she said to herself,
"Oh, that I had a child as white as snow, as red as blood, and as
black as the wood of the embroidery-frame!"

Not very long after she had a daughter, with a skin as white
as snow, lips as red as blood, and hair as black as ebony, and
she was named Snow-white. And when she was born the
queen died.

After a year had gone by the king took another wife, a beautiful woman, but proud and overbearing, and she could not
bear to be surpassed in beauty by any one. She had a magic

looking-glass, and she used to stand before it, and look in it, and say,

"Looking-glass upon the wall,
  Who is fairest of us all?"

And the looking-glass would answer,

"You are fairest of them all."

And she was contented, for she knew that the looking-glass spoke the truth.

Now, Snow-white was growing prettier and prettier, and when she was seven years old she was as beautiful as day, far more so than the queen herself. So one day when the queen went to her mirror and said,

"Looking-glass upon the wall,
  Who is fairest of us all?"

It answered,

"Queen, you are full fair, 'tis true,
  But Snow-white fairer is than you."

This gave the queen a great shock, and she became yellow and green with envy, and from that hour her heart turned against Snow-white, and she hated her. And envy and pride like ill weeds grew in her heart higher every day, until she had no peace day or night. At last she sent for a huntsman, and said,

"Take the child out into the woods, so that I may set eyes on her no more. You must put her to death, and bring me her heart for a token."

28

The huntsman consented, and led her away; but when he drew his cutlass to pierce Snow-white's innocent heart, she began to weep, and to say,

"Oh, dear huntsman, do not take my life. I will go away into the wild wood, and never come home again."

And as she was so lovely the huntsman had pity on her, and said,

"Away with you then, poor child"; for he thought the wild animals would be sure to devour her, and it was as if a stone had been rolled away from his heart when he spared to put her to death. Just at that moment a young wild boar came running by, so he caught and killed it, and taking out its heart, he brought it to the queen for a token. And it was salted and cooked, and the wicked woman ate it up, thinking that there was an end of Snow-white.

Now, when the poor child found herself quite alone in the wild woods, she felt full of terror, even of the very leaves on the trees, and she did not know what to do for fright. Then she began to run over the sharp stones and through the thorn bushes, and the wild beasts after her, but they did her no harm. She ran as long as her feet would carry her; and when the evening drew near she came to a little house, and she went inside to rest. Everything there was very small, but as pretty and clean as possible. There stood the little table ready laid, and covered with a white cloth, and seven little plates, and seven knives and forks, and drinking-cups. By the wall stood seven little beds, side by side, covered with clean white quilts. Snow-white, being very hungry and thirsty, ate from each plate a little porridge and bread, and drank out of each little cup a drop of wine, so

29

as not to finish up one portion alone. After that she felt so tired that she lay down on one of the beds, but it did not seem to suit her; one was too long, another too short, but at last the seventh was quite right; and so she lay down upon it, committed herself to heaven, and fell asleep.

When it was quite dark, the masters of the house came home. They were seven dwarfs, whose occupation was to dig underground among the mountains. When they had lighted their seven candles, and it was quite light in the little house, they saw that some one must have been in, as everything was not in the same order in which they left it. The first said,

"Who has been sitting in my little chair?"

The second said,

"Who has been eating from my little plate?"

The third said,

"Who has been taking my little loaf?"

The fourth said,

"Who has been tasting my porridge?"

The fifth said,

"Who has been using my little fork?"

The sixth said,

"Who has been cutting with my little knife?"

The seventh said,

"Who has been drinking from my little cup?"

Then the first one, looking round, saw a hollow in his bed, and cried,

"Who has been lying on my bed?"

And the others came running, and cried,

"Some one has been on our beds too!"

But when the seventh looked at his bed, he saw little Snow-white lying there asleep. Then he told the others, who came running up, crying out in their astonishment, and holding up their seven little candles to throw a light upon Snow-white.

"O goodness! O gracious!" cried they. "What beautiful child is this?" and were so full of joy to see her that they did not wake her, but let her sleep on. And the seventh dwarf slept with his comrades, an hour at a time with each, until the night had passed.

When it was morning, and Snow-white awoke and saw the seven dwarfs, she was very frightened; but they seemed quite friendly, and asked her what her name was, and she told them; and then they asked how she came to be in their house. And she related to them how her step-mother had wished her to be put to death, and how the huntsman had spared her life, and how she had run the whole day long, until at last she had found their little house. Then the dwarfs said,

"If you will keep our house for us, and cook, and wash, and make the beds, and sew and knit, and keep everything tidy and clean, you may stay with us, and you shall lack nothing."

"With all my heart," said Snow-white; and so she stayed, and kept the house in good order. In the morning the dwarfs went to the mountain to dig for gold; in the evening they came home, and their supper had to be ready for them. All the day long the maiden was left alone, and the good little dwarfs warned her, saying,

"Beware of your step-mother, she will soon know you are here. Let no one into the house."

Now the queen, having eaten Snow-white's heart, as she

supposed, felt quite sure that now she was the first and fairest, and so she came to her mirror, and said,

"Looking-glass upon the wall,
  Who is fairest of us all?"

And the glass answered,

"Queen, thou art of beauty rare,
  But Snow-white living in the glen
  With the seven little men,
  Is a thousand times more fair."

Then she was very angry, for the glass always spoke the truth, and she knew that the huntsman must have deceived her, and that Snow-white must still be living. And she thought and thought how she could manage to make an end of her, for as long as she was not the fairest in the land, envy left her no rest. At last she thought of a plan; she painted her face and dressed herself like an old pedlar woman, so that no one would have known her. In this disguise she went across the seven mountains, until she came to the house of the seven little dwarfs, and she knocked at the door and cried,

"Fine wares to sell! Fine wares to sell!"

Snow-white peeped out of the window and cried,

"Good-day, good woman, what have you to sell?"

"Good wares, fine wares," answered she, "laces of all colours"; and she held up a piece that was woven of variegated silk.

"I need not be afraid of letting in this good woman," thought

32

Snow-white, and she unbarred the door and bought the pretty lace.

"What a figure you are, child!" said the old woman. "Come and let me lace you properly for once."

Snow-white, suspecting nothing, stood up before her, and let her lace her with the new lace; but the old woman laced so quick and tight that it took Snow-white's breath away, and she fell down as dead.

"Now you have done with being the fairest," said the old woman as she hastened away.

Not long after that, towards evening, the seven dwarfs came home, and were terrified to see their dear Snow-white lying on the ground, without life or motion; they raised her up, and when they saw how tightly she was laced they cut the lace in two; then she began to draw breath, and little by little she returned to life. When the dwarfs heard what had happened they said,

"The old pedlar woman was no other than the wicked queen. You must beware of letting any one in when we are not here!"

And when the wicked woman got home she went to her glass and said,

"Looking-glass against the wall,
  Who is fairest of us all?"

   And it answered as before,

"Queen, thou art of beauty rare,
  But Snow-white living in the glen
  With the seven little men,
  Is a thousand times more fair."

When she heard that she was so struck with surprise that all the blood left her heart, for she knew that Snow-white must still be living.

"But now," said she, "I will think of something that will be her ruin." And by witchcraft she made a poisoned comb. Then she dressed herself up to look like another different sort of old woman. So she went across the seven mountains and came to the house of the seven dwarfs, and knocked at the door and cried,

"Good wares to sell! Good wares to sell!"

Snow-white looked out and said,

"Go away, I must not let anybody in."

"But you are not forbidden to look," said the old woman, taking out the poisoned comb and holding it up. It pleased the poor child so much that she was tempted to open the door; and when the bargain was made the old woman said,

"Now, for once your hair shall be properly combed."

Poor Snow-white, thinking no harm, let the old woman do as she would, but no sooner was the comb put in her hair than the poison began to work, and the poor girl fell down senseless.

"Now, you paragon of beauty," said the wicked woman, "this is the end of you," and went off. By good luck it was now near evening, and the seven little dwarfs came home. When they saw Snow-white lying on the ground as dead, they thought directly that it was the step-mother's doing, and looked about, found the poisoned comb, and no sooner had they drawn it out of her hair than Snow-white came to herself, and related all that had passed. Then they warned her once more to be

34

on her guard, and never again to let any one in at the door.

And the queen went home and stood before the looking-glass and said,

"Looking-glass against the wall,
 Who is fairest of us all?"

And the looking-glass answered as before,

"Queen, thou art of beauty rare,
 But Snow-white living in the glen
 With the seven little men,
 Is a thousand times more fair."

When she heard the looking-glass speak thus she trembled and shook with anger.

"Snow-white shall die," cried she, "though it should cost me my own life!" And then she went to a secret lonely chamber, where no one was likely to come, and there she made a poisonous apple. It was beautiful to look upon, being white with red cheeks, so that any one who should see it must long for it, but whoever ate even a little bit of it must die. When the apple was ready she painted her face and clothed herself like a peasant woman, and went across the seven mountains to where the seven dwarfs lived. And when she knocked at the door Snow-white put her head out of the window and said,

"I dare not let anybody in; the seven dwarfs told me not."

"All right," answered the woman; "I can easily get rid of my apples elsewhere. There, I will give you one."

"No," answered Snow-white, "I dare not take anything."

"Are you afraid of poison?" said the woman. "Look here.

I will cut the apple in two pieces; you shall have the red side, I will have the white one."

For the apple was so cunningly made, that all the poison was in the rosy half of it. Snow-white longed for the beautiful apple, and as she saw the peasant woman eating a piece of it she could no longer refrain, but stretched out her hand and took the poisoned half. But no sooner had she taken a morsel of it into her mouth than she fell to the earth as dead. And the queen, casting on her a terrible glance, laughed aloud and cried,

"As white as snow, as red as blood, as black as ebony! This time the dwarfs will not be able to bring you to life again."

And when she went home and asked the looking-glass,

"Looking-glass upon the wall,
  Who is fairest of us all?"

at last it answered,

"You are the fairest now of all."

Then her envious heart had peace, as much as an envious heart can have.

The dwarfs, when they came home in the evening, found Snow-white lying on the ground, and there came no breath out of her mouth, and she was dead. They lifted her up, sought if anything poisonous was to be found, cut her laces, combed her hair, washed her with water and wine, but all was of no avail, the poor child was dead, and remained dead. Then they laid her on a bier, and sat all seven of them round it, and wept and lamented three whole days. And then they would have buried her, but that she looked still as if she were living, with her beautiful blooming cheeks. So they said,

"We cannot hide her away in the black ground." And they had made a coffin of clear glass, so as to be looked into from all sides, and they laid her in it, and wrote in golden letters upon it her name, and that she was a king's daughter. Then they set the coffin out upon the mountain, and one of them always remained by it to watch. And the birds came too, and mourned for Snow-white, first an owl, then a raven, and lastly, a dove.

Now, for a long while Snow-white lay in the coffin and never changed, but looked as if she were asleep, for she was still as white as snow, as red as blood, and her hair was as black as ebony. It happened, however, that one day a king's son rode through the wood and up to the dwarfs' house, which was near it. He saw on the mountain the coffin, and beautiful Snow-white within it, and he read what was written in golden letters upon it. Then he said to the dwarfs,

"Let me have the coffin, and I will give you whatever you like to ask for it."

But the dwarfs told him that they could not part with it for all the gold in the world. But he said,

"I beseech you to give it me, for I cannot live without looking upon Snow-white; if you consent I will bring you to great honour, and care for you as if you were my brethren."

When he so spoke the good little dwarfs had pity upon him and gave him the coffin, and the king's son called his servants and bid them carry it away on their shoulders. Now it happened that as they were going along they stumbled over a bush, and with the shaking the bit of poisoned apple flew out of her throat. It was not long before she opened her eyes, threw up the cover of the coffin, and sat up, alive and well.

"Oh dear! Where am I?" cried she. The king's son answered, full of joy, "You are near me," and, relating all that had happened, he said,

"I would rather have you than anything in the world; come with me to my father's castle and you shall be my bride."

And Snow-white was kind, and went with him, and their wedding was held with pomp and great splendour.

But Snow-white's wicked step-mother was also bidden to the feast, and when she had dressed herself in beautiful clothes she went to her looking-glass and said,

"Looking-glass upon the wall,
  Who is fairest of us all?"

The looking-glass answered,

"O Queen, although you are of beauty rare,
  The young bride is a thousand times more fair."

Then she railed and cursed, and was beside herself with disappointment and anger. First she thought she would not go to the wedding; but then she felt she should have no peace until she went and saw the bride. And when she saw her she knew her for Snow-white, and could not stir from the place for anger and terror. For they had ready red-hot iron shoes, in which she had to dance until she fell down dead.

# Rumpelstiltskin

There was once a miller who was poor, but he had one beautiful daughter. It happened one day that he came to speak with the king, and to give himself consequence, he told him that he had a daughter who could spin gold out of straw. The king said to the miller,

"That is an art that pleases me well; if thy daughter is as clever as you say, bring her to my castle to-morrow, that I may put her to the proof."

When the girl was brought to him, he led her into a room that was quite full of straw, and gave her a wheel and spindle, and said,

"Now set to work, and if by the early morning thou hast not spun this straw to gold thou shalt die." And he shut the door himself, and left her there alone.

And so the poor miller's daughter was left there sitting, and could not think what to do for her life: she had no notion how to set to work to spin gold from straw, and her distress grew so great that she began to weep. Then all at once the door opened, and in came a little man, who said,

"Good evening, miller's daughter; why are you crying?"

"Oh!" answered the girl. "I have got to spin gold out of straw, and I don't understand the business."

Then the little man said,

"What will you give me if I spin it for you?"

"My necklace," said the girl.

The little man took the necklace, seated himself before the wheel, and whirr, whirr, whirr! three times round and the bobbin was full; then he took up another, and whirr, whirr, whirr; three times round, and that was full; and so he went on till the morning, when all the straw had been spun, and all the bobbins were full of gold. At sunrise came the king, and when he saw the gold he was astonished and very much rejoiced, for he was very avaricious. He had the miller's daughter taken into another room filled with straw, much bigger than the last, and told her that as she valued her life she must spin it all in one night. The girl did not know what to do, so she began to cry, and then the door opened, and the little man appeared and said,

"What will you give me if I spin all this straw into gold?"

"The ring from my finger," answered the girl.

So the little man took the ring, and began again to send the wheel whirring round, and by the next morning all the straw was spun into glistening gold. The king was rejoiced beyond measure at the sight, but as he could never have enough of gold, he had the miller's daughter taken into a still larger room full of straw, and said,

"This, too, must be spun in one night, and if you accomplish it you shall be my wife." For he thought, "Although she is but a miller's daughter, I am not likely to find any one richer in the whole world."

As soon as the girl was left alone, the little man appeared for the third time and said,

"What will you give me if I spin the straw for you this time?"

"I have nothing left to give," answered the girl.

"Then you must promise me the first child you have after you are queen," said the little man.

"But who knows whether that will happen?" thought the girl; but as she did not know what else to do in her necessity, she promised the little man what he desired, upon which he began to spin, until all the straw was gold. And when in the morning the king came and found all done according to his wish, he caused the wedding to be held at once, and the miller's pretty daughter became a queen.

In a year's time she brought a fine child into the world, and thought no more of the little man; but one day he came suddenly into her room, and said,

"Now give me what you promised me."

The queen was terrified greatly, and offered the little man all the riches of the kingdom if he would only leave the child; but the little man said,

"No, I would rather have something living than all the treasures of the world."

Then the queen began to lament and to weep, so that the little man had pity upon her.

"I will give you three days," said he, "and if at the end of that time you cannot tell my name, you must give up the child to me."

Then the queen spent the whole night in thinking over all the names that she had ever heard, and sent a messenger through the land to ask far and wide for all the names that could be found. And when the little man came next day (beginning with Caspar, Melchior, Balthazar), she repeated all she knew, and went through the whole list, but after each the little man said,

"That is not my name."

The second day the queen sent to inquire of all the neighbours what the servants were called, and told the little man all the most unusual and singular names, saying,

"Perhaps you are called Roast-ribs, or Sheepshanks, or Spindleshanks?" But he answered nothing but,

"That is not my name."

The third day the messenger came back again, and said,

"I have not been able to find one single new name; but as I passed through the woods I came to a high hill, and near it was a little house, and before the house burned a fire, and round the fire danced a comical little man, and he hopped on one leg and cried,

"To-day do I bake, to-morrow I brew,
  The day after that the queen's child comes in;

And oh! I am glad that nobody knew
That the name I am called is Rumpelstiltskin!"

You cannot think how pleased the queen was to hear that name, and soon afterwards, when the little man walked in and said, "Now, Mrs. Queen, what is my name?" she said at first,
"Are you called Jack?"
"No," he answered.
"Are you called Harry?" she asked again.
"No," answered he. And then she said,
"Then perhaps your name is Rumpelstiltskin!"
"The devil told you that! The devil told you that!" cried the little man, and in his anger he stamped with his right foot so hard that it went into the ground above his knee; then he seized his left foot with both his hands in such a fury that he split in two, and there was an end of him.

# The Golden Bird

In times gone by there was a king who had at the back of his castle a beautiful pleasure-garden, in which stood a tree that bore golden apples. As the apples ripened they were counted, but one morning one was missing. Then the king was angry, and he ordered that watch should be kept about the tree every night. Now the king had three sons, and he sent the eldest to spend the whole night in the garden; so he watched till midnight, and then he could keep off sleep no longer, and in the morning another apple was missing. The second son had to watch the following night; but it fared no better, for when twelve o'clock had struck he went to sleep, and in the morning another apple was missing. Now came the turn of the third son to watch, and he was ready to do so; but the king had less trust in him, and believed he would acquit himself still worse than his brothers, but in the end he consented to let him try. So the young man lay down under the tree to watch, and resolved that sleep should not be master. When it struck twelve something came rushing through the air, and he saw in the moonlight a bird flying towards him, whose feathers glittered like gold. The bird perched upon the tree, and had already pecked off an apple, when the young man let fly an arrow at it. The bird flew away, but the arrow had struck its plumage, and one of its golden feathers fell to the ground: the young man picked it up, and taking it next morning to the king, told him what had happened in the night. The king called his council together, and all declared that such a feather was worth more than the whole kingdom.

"Since the feather is so valuable," said the king, "one is not enough for me; I must and will have the whole bird."

So the eldest son set off, and relying on his own cleverness he thought he should soon find the golden bird. When he had gone some distance he saw a fox sitting at the edge of a wood, and he pointed his gun at him. The fox cried out,

"Do not shoot me, and I will give you good counsel. You are on your way to find the golden bird, and this evening you will come to a village, in which two taverns stand facing each other. One will be brightly lighted up, and there will be plenty of merriment going on inside; do not mind about that, but go into the other one, although it will look to you very uninviting."

"How can a silly beast give one any rational advice?" thought the king's son, and let fly at the fox, but missed him and he stretched out his tail and ran quick into the wood. Then the young man went on his way, and towards evening he came to the village, and there stood the two taverns; in one singing and dancing was going on, the other looked quite dull and wretched. "I should be a fool," said he, "to go into that dismal place, while there is anything so good close by." So he went into the merry inn, and there lived in clover, quite forgetting the bird and his father, and all good counsel.

As time went on, and the eldest son never came home, the second son set out to seek the golden bird. He met with the fox, just as the eldest did, and received good advice from him without attending to it. And when he came to the two taverns, his brother was standing and calling to him at the window of one of them, out of which came sounds of merriment; so he could not resist, but went in and revelled to his heart's content.

And then, as time went on, the youngest son wished to go forth, and to try his luck, but his father would not consent.

"It would be useless," said he; "he is much less likely to find the bird than his brothers, and if any misfortune were to happen to him he would not know how to help himself; his wits are none of the best."

But at last, as there was no peace to be had, he let him go. By the side of the wood sat the fox, begged him to spare his life, and gave him good counsel. The young man was kind, and said,

"Be easy, little fox, I will do you no harm."

"You shall not repent of it," answered the fox, "and that you may get there all the sooner, get up and sit on my tail."

And no sooner had he done so than the fox began to run, and off they went over stock and stone, so that the wind whistled in their hair. When they reached the village the young man got down, and, following the fox's advice, went into the

47

mean-looking tavern, without hesitating, and there he passed a quiet night. The next morning, when he went out into the field, the fox, who was sitting there already, said,

"I will tell you further what you have to do. Go straight on until you come to a castle, before which a great band of soldiers lie, but do not trouble yourself about them, for they will be asleep and snoring; pass through them and forward into the castle, and go through all the rooms, until you come to one where there is a golden bird hanging in a wooden cage. Near at hand will stand empty a golden cage of state, but you must beware of taking the bird out of his ugly cage and putting him into the fine one; if you do so you will come to harm."

After he had finished saying this the fox stretched out his tail again, and the king's son sat him down upon it; then away they went over stock and stone, so that the wind whistled through their hair. And when the king's son reached the castle he found everything as the fox had said: and he at last entered the room where the golden bird was hanging in a wooden cage, while a golden one was standing by; the three golden apples too were in the room. Then, thinking it foolish to let the beautiful bird stay in that mean and ugly cage, he opened the door of it, took hold of it, and put it in the golden one. In the same moment the bird uttered a piercing cry. The soldiers awaked, rushed in, seized the king's son and put him in prison. The next morning he was brought before a judge, and, as he confessed everything, condemned to death. But the king said he would spare his life on one condition, that he should bring him the golden horse whose paces were swifter than the wind, and that then he should also receive the golden bird as a reward.

So the king's son set off to find the golden horse, but he sighed, and was very sad, for how should it be accomplished? And then he saw his old friend the fox sitting by the roadside.

"Now, you see," said the fox, "all this has happened, because you would not listen to me. But be of good courage, I will bring you through, and will tell you how you are to get the golden horse. You must go straight on until you come to a castle, where the horse stands in his stable; before the stable-door the grooms will be lying, but they will all be asleep and snoring; and you can go and quietly lead out the horse. But one thing you must mind—take care to put upon him the plain saddle of wood and leather, and not the golden one, which will hang close by; otherwise it will go badly with you."

Then the fox stretched out his tail, and the king's son seated himself upon it, and away they went over stock and stone until the wind whistled through their hair. And everything happened just as the fox had said, and he came to the stall where the golden horse was: and as he was about to put on him the plain saddle, he thought to himself,

"Such a beautiful animal would be disgraced were I not to put on him the good saddle, which becomes him so well." However, no sooner did the horse feel the golden saddle touch him than he began to neigh. And the grooms all awoke, seized the king's son and threw him into prison. The next morning he was delivered up to justice and condemned to death, but the king promised him his life, and also to bestow upon him the

49

golden horse, if he could convey thither the beautiful princess of the golden castle.

With a heavy heart the king's son set out, but by great good luck he soon met with the faithful fox.

"I ought now to leave you to your own ill-luck," said the fox, "but I am sorry for you, and will once more help you in your need. Your way lies straight up to the golden castle: you will arrive there in the evening, and at night, when all is quiet, the beautiful princess goes to the bath. And as she is entering the bathing-house, go up to her and give her a kiss, then she will follow you, and you can lead her away; but do not suffer her first to go and take leave of her parents, or it will go ill with you."

Then the fox stretched out his tail; the king's son seated himself upon it, and away they went over stock and stone, so that the wind whistled through their hair. And when he came to the golden castle all was as the fox had said. He waited until midnight, when all lay in deep sleep, and then as the beautiful princess went to the bathing-house he went up to her and gave her a kiss, and she willingly promised to go with him, but she begged him earnestly, and with tears, that he would let her first go and take leave of her parents. At first he denied her prayer, but as she wept so much the more, and fell at his feet, he gave in at last. And no sooner had the princess reached her father's bedside than he, and all who were in the castle, waked up, and the young man was seized and thrown into prison.

The next morning the king said to him,

"Thy life is forfeit, but thou shalt find grace if thou canst level that mountain that lies before my windows, and over which I am not able to see: and if this is done within eight days thou shalt have my daughter for a reward."

So the king's son set to work, and dug and shovelled away without ceasing, but when, on the seventh day, he saw how little he had accomplished, and that all his work was as nothing, he fell into great sadness, and gave up all hope. But on the evening of the seventh day the fox appeared, and said,

"You do not deserve that I should help you, but go now and lie down to sleep, and I will do the work for you."

The next morning when he awoke, and looked out of the window, the mountain had disappeared. The young man hastened full of joy to the king, and told him that his behest was fulfilled, and, whether the king liked it or not, he had to keep to his word, and let his daughter go.

So they both went away together, and it was not long before the faithful fox came up to them.

"Well, you have got the best first," said he; "but you must know the golden horse belongs to the princess of the golden castle."

"But how shall I get it?" asked the young man.

"I am going to tell you," answered the fox. "First, go to the king who sent you to the golden castle, and take to him the beautiful princess. There will then be very great rejoicing; he will willingly give you the golden horse, and they will lead him out to you; then mount him without delay, and stretch out your hand to each of them to take leave, and last of all to the princess, and when you have her by the hand swing her up on

51

the horse behind you, and off you go! Nobody will be able to overtake you, for that horse goes swifter than the wind."

And so it was all happily done, and the king's son carried off the beautiful princess on the golden horse. The fox did not stay behind, and he said to the young man,

"Now, I will help you to get the golden bird. When you draw near the castle where the bird is, let the lady alight, and I will take her under my care; then you must ride the golden horse into the castle-yard, and there will be great rejoicing to see it, and they will bring out to you the golden bird; as soon as you have the cage in your hand, you must start off back to us, and then you shall carry the lady away."

The plan was successfully carried out; and when the young man returned with the treasure, the fox said,

"Now what will you give me for my reward?"

"What would you like?" asked the young man.

"When we are passing through the wood, I desire that you should slay me, and cut my head and feet off."

"That were a strange sign of gratitude," said the king's son, "and I could not possibly do such a thing."

Then said the fox,

"If you will not do it, I must leave you; but before I go let me give you some good advice. Beware of two things: buy no gallows-meat, and sit at no brook-side." With that the fox ran off into the wood.

The young man thought to himself, "That is a wonderful animal, with most singular ideas. How should any one buy gallows-meat? And I am sure I have no particular fancy for sitting by a brook-side."

So he rode on with the beautiful princess, and their way led them through the village where his two brothers had stayed. There they heard great outcry and noise, and when he asked what it was all about, they told him that two people were going to be hanged. And when he drew near he saw that it was his two brothers who had done all sorts of evil tricks, and had wasted all their goods. He asked if there were no means of setting them free.

"Oh yes! If you will buy them off," answered the people; "but why should you spend your money in redeeming such worthless men?"

But he persisted in doing so; and when they were let go they all went on their journey together.

After a while they came to the wood where the fox had met them first, and there it seemed so cool and sheltered from the sun's burning rays that the two brothers said,

"Let us rest here for a little by the brook, and eat and drink to refresh ourselves."

The young man consented, quite forgetting the fox's warning, and he seated himself by the brook-side, suspecting no evil. But the two brothers thrust him backwards into the brook, seized the princess, the horse, and the bird, and went home to their father.

"Is not this the golden bird that we bring?" said they. "And we have also the golden horse, and the princess of the golden castle."

Then there was great rejoicing in the royal castle, but the horse did not feed, the bird did not chirp, and the princess sat still and wept.

The youngest brother, however, had not perished. The brook was, by good fortune, dry, and he fell on soft moss without receiving any hurt, but he could not get up again. But in his need the faithful fox was not lacking; he came up running, and reproached him for having forgotten his advice.

"But I cannot forsake you all the same," said he. "I will help you back again into daylight." So he told the young man to grasp his tail, and hold on to it fast, and so he drew him up again.

"Still you are not quite out of all danger," said the fox. "Your brothers, not being certain of your death, have surrounded the wood with sentinels, who are to put you to death if you let yourself be seen."

A poor beggar-man was sitting by the path, and the young man changed clothes with him, and went clad in that wise into the king's courtyard. Nobody knew him, but the bird began to chirp, and the horse began to feed, and the beautiful princess ceased weeping.

"What does this mean?" said the king, astonished.

The princess answered,

"I cannot tell, except that I was sad, and now I am joyful; it is to me as if my rightful bridegroom had returned."

Then she told him all that happened, although the two brothers had threatened to put her to death if she let out anything. The king then ordered every person who was in the castle to be brought before him, and with the rest came the young man like a beggar in his wretched garments; but the princess knew him, and greeted him well, falling on his neck and kissing him. The wicked brothers were seized and put to death, and the youngest brother was married to the princess, and succeeded to the inheritance of his father.

But what became of the poor fox? Long afterwards the king's son was going through the wood, and the fox met him and said,

"Now, you have everything that you can wish for, but my misfortunes never come to an end, and it lies in your power to free me from them." And once more he prayed the king's son earnestly to slay him, and cut off his head and feet. So, at last, he consented, and no sooner was it done than the fox was changed into a man, and was no other than the brother of the beautiful princess; and thus he was set free from a spell that had bound him for a long, long time.

And now, indeed, there lacked nothing to their happiness as long as they lived.

# The Golden Goose

There was a man who had three sons, the youngest of whom was called the Simpleton, and was despised, laughed at, and neglected, on every occasion. It happened one day that the eldest son wished to go into the forest to cut wood, and before he went his mother gave him a delicious pancake and a flask of wine, that he might not suffer from hunger or thirst. When he came into the forest a little grey man met him, who wished him good day, and said,

"Give me a bit of cake out of your pocket, and let me have a drink of your wine; I am so hungry and thirsty."

But the prudent youth answered,

"Give you my cake and my wine? I haven't got any; be off with you."

And leaving the little man standing there, he went off. Then he began to fell a tree, but he had not been at it long before he made a wrong stroke, and the hatchet hit him in the arm, so that he was obliged to go home and get it bound up. That was what came of the little grey man.

Afterwards the second son went into the wood, and the mother gave to him, as to the eldest, a pancake and a flask of wine. The little old grey man met him also, and begged for a little bit of cake and a drink of wine. But the second son spoke out plainly, saying,

"What I give you I lose myself, so be off with you."

And leaving the little man standing there, he went off. The punishment followed; as he was chopping away at the tree, he hit himself in the leg so severely that he had to be carried home.

Then said the Simpleton,

"Father, let me go for once into the forest to cut wood." And the father answered, "Your brothers have hurt themselves by so doing; give it up, you understand nothing about it."

But the Simpleton went on begging so long that the father said at last,

"Well, be off with you; you will only learn by experience."

The mother gave him a cake (it was only made with water, and baked in the ashes), and with it a flask of sour beer. When he came into the forest the little old grey man met him, and greeted him, saying,

"Give me a bit of your cake, and a drink from your flask; I am so hungry and thirsty."

And the Simpleton answered, "I have only a flour and water cake and sour beer, but if that is good enough for you, let us sit down together and eat." Then they sat down, and as the Simpleton took out his flour and water cake it became a rich pancake, and his sour beer became good wine; then they ate and drank, and afterwards the little man said,

"As you have such a kind heart, and share what you have so willingly, I will bestow good luck upon you. Yonder stands an old tree; cut it down, and at its roots you will find something," and thereupon the little man took his departure.

The Simpleton went there, and hewed away at the tree, and when it fell he saw, sitting among the roots, a goose with feathers of pure gold. He lifted it out and took it with him to an inn where he intended to stay the night. The landlord had three daughters who, when they saw the goose, were curious to know what wonderful kind of bird it was, and ended by longing for one of its golden feathers. The eldest thought, "I will wait for a good opportunity, and then I will pull out one of its feathers for myself"; and so, when the Simpleton was gone out, she seized the goose by its wing—but there her finger and hand had to stay, held fast. Soon after came the second sister with the same idea of plucking out one of the golden feathers for herself; but scarcely had she touched her sister, than she also was obliged to stay, held fast. Lastly came the third with the same intentions; but the other screamed out,

"Stay away! For heaven's sake stay away!"

But she did not see why she should stay away, and thought, "If they do so, why should not I?" and went towards them. But when she reached her sisters there she stopped, hanging on with them. And so they had to stay, all night. The next morning the Simpleton took the goose under his arm and went away, unmindful of the three girls that hung on to it. The three had always to run after him, left and right, wherever his legs carried

59

him. In the midst of the fields they met the parson, who, when he saw the procession, said,

"Shame on you, girls, running after a young fellow through the fields like this," and forthwith he seized hold of the youngest by the hand to drag her away, but hardly had he touched her when he too was obliged to run after them himself. Not long after the sexton came that way, and seeing the respected parson following at the heels of the three girls, he called out,

"Ho, your reverence, whither away so quickly? You forget that we have another christening to-day"; and he seized hold of him by his gown; but no sooner had he touched him than he was obliged to follow on too. As the five tramped on, one after another, two peasants with their hoes came up from the fields, and the parson cried out to them, and begged them to come and set him and the sexton free, but no sooner had they touched the sexton than they had to follow on too; and now there were seven following the Simpleton and the goose.

By and by they came to a town where a king reigned, who had an only daughter who was so serious that no one could make her laugh; therefore the king had given out that whoever should make her laugh should have her in marriage. The Simpleton, when he heard this, went with his goose and his hangers-on into the presence of the king's daughter, and as soon as she saw the seven people following always one after the other, she burst out laughing, and seemed as if she could never stop. And so the Simpleton earned a right to her as his bride; but the king did not like him for a son-in-law and made all kinds of objections, and said he must first bring a man who could drink a whole cellar of wine. The Simpleton thought that the little grey man would be able to help him, and went out into the forest, and there, on the very spot where he felled the tree, he saw a man sitting with a very sad countenance. The Simpleton asked him what was the matter, and he answered,

"I have a great thirst, which I cannot quench: cold water does not agree with me; I have indeed drunk a whole cask of wine, but what good is a drop like that?"

Then said the Simpleton,

"I can help you; only come with me, and you shall have enough."

He took him straight to the king's cellar, and the man sat himself down before the big vats, and drank, and drank, and before a day was over he had drunk up the whole cellar-full. The Simpleton again asked for his bride, but the king was annoyed that a wretched fellow, called the Simpleton by everybody, should carry off his daughter, and so he made new conditions. He was to produce a man who could eat a mountain of bread. The Simpleton did not hesitate long, but ran quickly off to the forest, and there in the same place sat a man who had fastened a strap round his body, making a very piteous face, and saying,

"I have eaten a whole bakehouse full of rolls, but what is the use of that when one is so hungry as I am? My stomach feels quite empty, and I am obliged to strap myself together, that I may not die of hunger."

The Simpleton was quite glad of this, and said,

"Get up quickly, and come along with me, and you shall have enough to eat."

He led him straight to the king's courtyard, where all the

meal in the kingdom had been collected and baked into a mountain of bread. The man out of the forest settled himself down before it and hastened to eat, and in one day the whole mountain had disappeared.

Then the Simpleton asked for his bride the third time. The king, however, found one more excuse, and said he must have a ship that should be able to sail on land or on water.

"So soon," said he, "as you come sailing along with it, you shall have my daughter for your wife."

The Simpleton went straight to the forest, and there sat the little old grey man with whom he had shared his cake, and he said,

"I have eaten for you, and I have drunk for you, I will also give you the ship; and all because you were kind to me at the first."

Then he gave him the ship that could sail on land and on water, and when the king saw it he knew he could no longer withhold his daughter. The marriage took place immediately, and at the death of the king the Simpleton possessed the kingdom, and lived long and happily with his wife.

# The White Snake

A long time ago there lived a King whose wisdom was noised abroad in all the country. Nothing remained long unknown to him, and it was as if the knowledge of hidden things was brought to him in the air. However, he had one curious custom. Every day at dinner, after the table had been cleared and every one gone away, a trusty servant had to bring in one other dish. But it was covered up, and the servant himself did not know what was in it, and no one else knew, for the King waited until he was quite alone before he uncovered it. This had gone on a long time, but at last there came a day when the servant could restrain his curiosity no longer, but as he was carrying the dish away he took it into his own room. As soon as he had fastened the door securely, he lifted the cover, and there was a white snake lying on the dish. After seeing it he could not resist the desire to taste it, and so he cut off a small piece and put it in his mouth.

As soon as it touched his tongue he heard outside his window a strange chorus of delicate voices. He went and listened, and found that it was the sparrows talking together, and telling each other all they had seen in the fields and woods. The virtue of the snake had given him power to understand the speech of animals.

Now it happened one day that the Queen lost her most splendid ring, and suspicion fell upon the trusty servant, who had the general superintendence, and he was accused of stealing it. The King summoned him to his presence, and after many reproaches told him that if by the next day he was not able to name the thief he should be considered guilty, and punished. It was in vain that he protested his innocence; he could get no better sentence. In his uneasiness and anxiety he went out into the courtyard, and began to consider what he could do in so great a necessity. There sat the ducks by the running water and rested themselves, and plumed themselves with their flat bills, and held a comfortable chat. The servant stayed where he was and listened to them. They told how they had waddled about all yesterday morning and found good food; and then one of them said pitifully,

"Something lies very heavy in my craw—it is the ring that was lying under the Queen's window; I swallowed it down in too great a hurry."

Then the servant seized her by the neck, took her into the kitchen, and said to the cook,

"Kill this one, she is quite ready for cooking."

"Yes," said the cook, weighing it in her hand; "there will be no trouble of fattening this one—it has been ready ever so long."

She then slit up its neck, and when it was opened the Queen's ring was found in its craw. The servant could now clearly prove his innocence, and in order to make up for the injustice he had suffered the King permitted him to ask some favour for himself, and also promised him the place of greatest honour in the royal household.

But the servant refused it, and only asked for a horse and money for travelling, for he had a fancy to see the world, and look about him a little. So his request was granted, and he set out on his way; and one day he came to a pool of water, by which he saw three fishes who had got entangled in the rushes, and were panting for water. Although fishes are usually considered dumb creatures, he understood very well their lament that they were to perish so miserably; and as he had a compassionate heart he dismounted from his horse, and put the three fishes back again into the water. They quivered all over with joy, stretched out their heads, and called out to him,

"We will remember and reward thee, because thou hast delivered us." He rode on, and after a while he heard a small voice come up from the sand underneath his horse's feet. He listened, and understood how an ant-king was complaining,

"If only these men would keep off, with their great awkward beasts! Here comes this stupid horse treading down my people with his hard hoofs!"

The man then turned his horse to the side-path, and the ant-king called out to him,

"We will remember and reward thee!"

65

The path led him through a wood, and there he saw a father-raven and mother-raven standing by their nest and throwing their young ones out.

"Off with you! Young gallows-birds!" cried they. "We cannot stuff you any more; you are big enough to fend for yourselves!" The poor young ravens lay on the ground, fluttering, and beating the air with their pinions, and crying,

"We are poor helpless things, we cannot fend for ourselves, we cannot even fly! We can only die of hunger!"

Then the kind young man dismounted, killed his horse with his dagger, and left it to the young ravens for food. They came hopping up, feasted away at it, and cried,

"We will remember and reward thee!"

So now he had to use his own legs, and when he had gone a long way he came to a great town. There was much noise and thronging in the streets, and there came a man on a horse, who proclaimed,

"That the King's daughter seeks a husband, but he who wishes to marry her must perform a difficult task, and if he cannot carry it through successfully, he must lose his life."

Many had already tried, but had lost their lives, in vain. The young man, when he saw the King's daughter, was so dazzled by her great beauty, that he forgot all danger, went to the King and offered himself as a wooer.

Then he was led to the sea-side, and a gold ring was thrown into the water before his eyes. Then the King told him that he must fetch the ring up again from the bottom of the sea, saying,

"If you come back without it, you shall be put under the waves again and again until you are drowned."

Every one pitied the handsome young man, but they went and left him alone by the sea. As he was standing on the shore and thinking of what he should do, there came three fishes swimming by, none other than those he had set free. The middle one had a mussel in his mouth, and he laid it on the strand at the young man's feet; and when he took it up and opened it there was the gold ring inside! Full of joy he carried it to the King, and expected the promised reward; but the King's daughter, proud of her high birth, despised him, and set him another task to perform. She went out into the garden, and strewed about over the grass ten sacks full of millet seed.

"By the time the sun rises in the morning you must have picked up all these," she said, "and not a grain must be wanting."

The young man sat down in the garden and considered how it was possible to do this task, but he could contrive nothing, and stayed there, feeling very sorrowful, and expecting to be led to death at break of day. But when the first beams of the sun fell on the garden he saw that the ten sacks were all filled, standing one by the other, and not even a grain was missing. The ant-king had arrived in the night with his thousands of ants, and the grateful creatures had picked up all the millet seed, and filled the sacks with great industry. The King's daughter came herself into the garden and saw with astonishment that the young man had performed all that had been given him to do. But she could not let her proud heart melt, and said,

"Although he has completed the two tasks, he shall not be my bridegroom unless he brings me an apple from the tree of life."

The young man did not know where the tree of life was to be found, but he set out and went on and on, as long as his legs could carry him, but he had no hope of finding it. When he had gone through three kingdoms he came one evening to a wood, and seated himself under a tree to go to sleep; but he heard a rustling in the boughs, and a golden apple fell into his hand. Immediately three ravens flew towards him, perched on his knee, and said,

"We are the three young ravens that you delivered from starving; when we grew big, and heard you were seeking the golden apple, we flew over the sea to the end of the earth, where the tree of life stands, and we fetched the apple."

Full of joy the young man set off on his way home, and brought the golden apple to the King's beautiful daughter, who was without any further excuse.

So they divided the apple of life, and ate it together; and their hearts were filled with love, and they lived in undisturbed happiness to a great age.

# Little Red Riding Hood

There was once a sweet little maid, much beloved by everybody, but most of all by her grandmother, who never knew how to make enough of her. Once she sent her a little cap of red velvet, and as it was very becoming to her, and she never wore anything else, people called her Little Red Riding Hood. One day her mother said to her,

"Come, Little Red Riding Hood, here are some cakes and a flask of wine for you to take to grandmother; she is weak and ill, and they will do her good. Make haste and start before it grows hot, and walk properly and nicely, and don't run, or you might fall and break the flask of wine, and there would be none left for grandmother. And when you go into her room, don't forget to say, Good morning, instead of staring about you."

"I will be sure to take care," said Little Red Riding Hood to her mother, and gave her hand upon it. Now the grandmother lived away in the wood, half-an-hour's walk from the village; and when Little Red Riding Hood had reached the wood, she met the wolf; but as she did not know what a bad sort of animal he was, she did not feel frightened.

"Good day, Little Red Riding Hood," said he.

"Thank you kindly, Wolf," answered she.

"Where are you going so early, Little Red Riding Hood?"

"To my grandmother's."

"What are you carrying under your apron?"

"Cakes and wine; we baked yesterday; and my grandmother is very weak and ill, so they will do her good, and strengthen her."

"Where does your grandmother live, Little Red Riding Hood?"

"A quarter of an hour's walk from here; her house stands beneath the three oak trees, and you may know it by the hazel bushes," said Little Red Riding Hood. The wolf thought to himself,

"That tender young thing would be a delicious morsel, and would taste better than the old one; I must manage somehow to get both of them."

Then he walked by Little Red Riding Hood a little while, and said,

"Little Red Riding Hood, just look at the pretty flowers that are growing all around you, and I don't think you are listening to the song of the birds; you are posting along just as if you were going to school, and it is so delightful out here in the wood."

Little Red Riding Hood glanced round her, and when she

saw the sunbeams darting here and there through the trees, and lovely flowers everywhere, she thought to herself,

"If I were to take a fresh nosegay to my grandmother she would be very pleased, and it is so early in the day that I shall reach her in plenty of time"; and so she ran about in the wood, looking for flowers. And as she picked one she saw a still prettier one a little farther off, and so she went farther and farther into the wood. But the wolf went straight to the grandmother's house and knocked at the door.

"Who is there?" cried the grandmother.

"Little Red Riding Hood," he answered, "and I have brought you some cake and wine. Please open the door."

"Lift the latch," cried the grandmother; "I am too feeble to get up."

So the wolf lifted the latch, and the door flew open, and he fell on the grandmother and ate her up without saying one word. Then he drew on her clothes, put on her cap, lay down in her bed, and drew the curtains.

Little Red Riding Hood was all this time running about among the flowers, and when she had gathered as many as she could hold, she remembered her grandmother, and set off to go to her. She was surprised to find the door standing open, and when she came inside she felt very strange, and thought to herself,

"Oh dear, how uncomfortable I feel, and I was so glad this morning to go to my grandmother!"

And when she said, "Good morning," there was no answer. Then she went up to the bed and drew back the curtains; there

71

lay the grandmother with her cap pulled over her eyes, so that she looked very odd.

"O grandmother, what large ears you have got!"

"The better to hear with."

"O grandmother, what great eyes you have got!"

"The better to see with."

"O grandmother, what large hands you have got!"

"The better to take hold of you with."

"But, grandmother, what a terrible large mouth you have got!"

"The better to devour you!" And no sooner had the wolf said it than he made one bound from the bed, and swallowed up poor Little Red Riding Hood.

Then the wolf, having satisfied his hunger, lay down again in the bed, went to sleep, and began to snore loudly. The huntsman heard him as he was passing by the house, and thought,

"How the old woman snores—I had better see if there is anything the matter with her."

Then he went into the room, and walked up to the bed, and saw the wolf lying there.

"At last I find you, you old sinner!" said he. "I have been looking for you a long time." And he made up his mind that the wolf had swallowed the grandmother whole, and that she might yet be saved. So he did not fire, but took a pair of shears and began to slit up the wolf's body. When he made a few snips Little Red Riding Hood appeared, and after a few more snips she jumped out and cried, "Oh dear, how frightened I have been! It is so dark inside the wolf." And then out came the old grandmother, still living and breathing. But Little Red

Riding Hood went and quickly fetched some large stones, with which she filled the wolf's body, so that when he waked up, and was going to rush away, the stones were so heavy that he sank down and fell dead.

They were all three very pleased. The huntsman took off the wolf's skin, and carried it home. The grandmother ate the cakes, and drank the wine, and held up her head again, and Little Red Riding Hood said to herself that she would never more stray about in the wood alone, but would mind what her mother told her.

It must also be related how a few days afterwards, when Little Red Riding Hood was again taking cakes to her grandmother, another wolf spoke to her, and wanted to tempt her to leave the path; but she was on her guard, and went straight on her way, and told her grandmother how that the wolf had met her, and wished her good-day, but had looked so wicked about the eyes that she thought if it had not been on the high road he would have devoured her.

"Come," said the grandmother, "we will shut the door, so that he may not get in."

Soon after came the wolf knocking at the door, and calling out, "Open the door, grandmother, I am Little Red Riding Hood, bringing you cakes." But they remained still, and did not open the door. After that the wolf slunk by the house, and got at last upon the roof to wait until Little Red Riding Hood should return home in the evening; then he meant to spring down upon her, and devour her in the darkness. But the grandmother discovered his plot. Now there stood before the house a great stone trough, and the grandmother said to the child, "Lit-

73

tle Red Riding Hood, I was boiling sausages yesterday, so take the bucket, and carry away the water they were boiled in, and pour it into the trough."

And Little Red Riding Hood did so until the great trough was quite full. When the smell of the sausages reached the nose of the wolf he snuffed it up, and looked round, and stretched out his neck so far that he lost his balance and began to slip, and he slipped down off the roof straight into the great trough, and was drowned. Then Little Red Riding Hood went cheerfully home, and came to no harm.

# The Bremen Town Musicians

There was once an ass whose master had made him carry sacks
to the mill for many a long year, but whose strength began at
last to fail, so that each day as it came found him less capable of
work. Then his master began to think of turning him out, but
the ass, guessing that something was in the wind that boded
him no good, ran away, taking the road to Bremen; for there
he thought he might get an engagement as town musician.
When he had gone a little way he found a hound lying by the
side of the road panting, as if he had run a long way.

"Now, Holdfast, what are you so out of breath about?" said
the ass.

"Oh dear!" said the dog. "Now I am old, I get weaker every
day, and can do no good in the hunt, so, as my master was
going to have me killed, I have made my escape; but now, how
am I to gain a living?"

75

"I will tell you what," said the ass. "I am going to Bremen to become town musician. You may as well go with me, and take up music too. I can play the lute, and you can beat the drum."

And the dog consented, and they walked on together. It was not long before they came to a cat sitting in the road, looking as dismal as three wet days.

"Now then, what is the matter with you, old shaver?" said the ass.

"I should like to know who would be cheerful when his neck is in danger?" answered the cat. "Now that I am old my teeth are getting blunt, and I would rather sit by the oven and purr than run about after mice, and my mistress wanted to drown me; so I took myself off; but good advice is scarce, and I do not know what is to become of me."

"Go with us to Bremen," said the ass, "and become town musician. You understand serenading."

The cat thought well of the idea, and went with them accordingly. After that the three travellers passed by a yard, and a cock was perched on the gate crowing with all his might.

"Your cries are enough to pierce bone and marrow," said the ass. "What is the matter?"

"I have foretold good weather for Lady-day, so that all the shirts may be washed and dried; and now on Sunday morning company is coming, and the mistress has told the cook that I must be made into soup, and this evening my neck is to be wrung, so that I am crowing with all my might while I can."

"You had much better go with us, Chanticleer," said the ass. "We are going to Bremen. At any rate that will be better than dying. You have a powerful voice, and when we are all performing together it will have a very good effect."

So the cock consented, and they went on all four together.

But Bremen was too far off to be reached in one day, and towards evening they came to a wood, where they determined to pass the night. The ass and the dog lay down under a large tree; the cat got up among the branches, and the cock flew up to the top, as that was the safest place for him. Before he went to sleep he looked all round him to the four points of the compass, and perceived in the distance a little light shining, and he called out to his companions that there must be a house not far off, as he could see a light, so the ass said,

"We had better get up and go there, for these are uncomfortable quarters." The dog began to fancy a few bones, not quite bare, would do him good. And they all set off in the direction of the light, and it grew larger and brighter, until at last it led them to a robber's house, all lighted up. The ass, being the biggest, went up to the window, and looked in.

"Well, what do you see?" asked the dog.

"What do I see?" answered the ass. "Here is a table set out with splendid eatables and drinkables, and robbers sitting at it and making themselves very comfortable."

"That would just suit us," said the cock.

"Yes, indeed, I wish we were there," said the ass. Then they consulted together how it should be managed so as to get the robbers out of the house, and at last they hit on a plan. The ass was to place his forefeet on the window-sill, the dog was to get on the ass's back, the cat on the top of the dog, and lastly the cock was to fly up and perch on the cat's head. When that was done, at a given signal they all began to perform their music. The ass brayed, the dog barked, the cat mewed, and the cock crowed; then they burst through into the room, breaking all the panes of glass. The robbers fled at the dreadful sound; they thought it was some goblin, and fled to the wood in the utmost terror. Then the four companions sat down to table, made free with the remains of the meal, and feasted as if they had been hungry for a month. And when they had finished they put out the lights, and each sought out a sleeping-place to suit his nature and habits. The ass laid himself down outside on the dunghill, the dog behind the door, the cat on the hearth by the warm ashes, and the cock settled himself in the cockloft, and as they were all tired with their long journey they soon fell fast asleep.

When midnight drew near, and the robbers from afar saw that no light was burning, and that everything appeared quiet, their captain said to them that he thought that they had run away without reason, telling one of them to go and reconnoitre. So one of them went, and found everything quite quiet; he went into the kitchen to strike a light, and taking the glowing fiery eyes of the cat for burning coals, he held a match to them in order to kindle it. But the cat, not seeing the joke, flew into his face, spitting and scratching. Then he cried out in terror, and ran to get out at the back-door, but the dog, who was lying there, ran at him and bit his leg; and as he was rushing through the yard by the dunghill the ass struck out and gave him a great kick with his hindfoot; and the cock, who had been wakened with the noise, and felt quite brisk, cried out, "Cock-a-doodle-doo!"

Then the robber got back as well as he could to his captain, and said, "Oh dear! In that house there is a grewsome witch, and I felt her breath and her long nails in my face; and by the door there stands a man who stabbed me in the leg with a knife; and in the yard there lies a black spectre, who beat me with his wooden club; and above, upon the roof, there sits the justice, who cried, 'Bring that rogue here!' And so I ran away from the place as fast as I could."

From that time forward the robbers never ventured to that house, and the four Bremen town musicians found themselves so well off where they were, that there they stayed. And the person who last related this tale is still living, as you see.

# Prudent Hans

One day, Hans's mother said, "Where are you going, Hans?"
Hans answered,
"To Grethel's, mother."
"Manage well, Hans."
"All right! Good-bye, mother."
"Good-bye, Hans."
Then Hans came to Grethel's.
"Good morning, Grethel."
"Good morning, Hans. What have you brought me to-day?"
"I have brought nothing, but I want something."
So Grethel gave Hans a needle; and then he said,
"Good-bye, Grethel," and she said, "Good-bye, Hans."
Hans carried the needle away with him, and stuck it in a hay-cart that was going along, and he followed it home.
"Good evening, mother."

"Good evening, Hans. Where have you been?"

"To Grethel's, mother."

"What did you take her?"

"I took nothing, but I brought away something."

"What did Grethel give you?"

"A needle, mother."

"What did you do with it, Hans?"

"Stuck it in the hay-cart."

"That was very stupid of you, Hans. You should have stuck it in your sleeve."

"All right, mother! I'll do better next time."

When next time came, Hans's mother said,

"Where are you going, Hans?"

"To Grethel's, mother."

"Manage well, Hans."

"All right! Good-bye, mother."

"Good-bye, Hans."

Then Hans came to Grethel's.

"Good morning, Grethel."

"Good morning, Hans. What have you brought me to-day?"

"I've brought nothing, but I want something."

So Grethel gave Hans a knife, and then he said, "Good-bye, Grethel," and she said, "Good-bye, Hans."

Hans took the knife away with him, and stuck it in his sleeve, and went home.

"Good evening, mother."

"Good evening, Hans. Where have you been?"

"To Grethel's."

"What did you take her?"

"I took nothing, but I brought away something."

"What did Grethel give you, Hans?"

"A knife, mother."

"What did you do with it, Hans?"

"Stuck it in my sleeve, mother."

"That was very stupid of you, Hans. You should have put it in your pocket."

"All right, mother! I'll do better next time."

When next time came, Hans's mother said,

"Where to, Hans?"

"To Grethel's, mother."

"Manage well, Hans."

"All right! Good-bye, mother."

"Good-bye, Hans."

So Hans came to Grethel's. "Good morning, Grethel."

"Good morning, Hans. What have you brought me to-day?"

"I've brought nothing, but I want to take away something."

So Grethel gave Hans a young goat; then he said,

"Good-bye, Grethel," and she said, "Good-bye, Hans."

So Hans carried off the goat, and tied its legs together, and put it in his pocket, and by the time he got home it was suffocated.

"Good evening, mother."

"Good evening, Hans. Where have you been?"

"To Grethel's, mother."

"What did you take her, Hans?"

"I took nothing, but I brought away something."

"What did Grethel give you, Hans?"

"A goat, mother."

"What did you do with it, Hans?"

"Put it in my pocket, mother."

"That was very stupid of you, Hans. You should have tied a cord round its neck, and led it home."

"All right, mother! I'll do better next time."

Then when next time came, .

"Where to, Hans?"

"To Grethel's, mother."

"Manage well, Hans."

"All right! Good-bye, mother."

"Good-bye, Hans."

Then Hans came to Grethel's.

"Good morning, Grethel."

"Good morning, Hans. What have you brought me to-day?"

"I've brought nothing, but I want to take away something."

So Grethel gave Hans a piece of bacon. Then he said, "Good-bye, Grethel."

She said, "Good-bye, Hans."

Hans took the bacon and tied a string round it, and dragged it after him on his way home, and the dogs came and ate it up, so that when he got home he had the string in his hand, and nothing at the other end of it.

"Good evening, mother."

"Good evening, Hans. Where have you been?"

"To Grethel's, mother."

"What did you take her, Hans?"

"I took her nothing, but I brought away something."

"What did Grethel give you, Hans?"

"A piece of bacon, mother." .

"What did you do with it, Hans?"

"I tied a piece of string to it, and led it home, but the dogs ate it, mother."

"That was very stupid of you, Hans. You ought to have carried it on your head."

"All right! I'll do better next time, mother."

When next time came,

"Where to, Hans?"

"To Grethel's, mother."

"Manage well, Hans."

"All right! Good-bye, mother."

"Good-bye, Hans."

Then Hans came to Grethel's.

"Good morning, Grethel."

"Good morning, Hans. What have you brought me?"

"I have brought nothing, but I want to take away something."

So Grethel gave Hans a calf.

"Good-bye, Grethel."

"Good-bye, Hans."

Hans took the calf, and set it on his head, and carried it home, and the calf scratched his face.

"Good evening, mother."

"Good evening, Hans. Where have you been?"

"To Grethel's, mother."

"What did you take her?"

"I took nothing, but I brought away something."

"What did Grethel give you, Hans?"

"A calf, mother."

"What did you do with the calf, Hans?"

"I carried it home on my head, but it scratched my face."

"That was very stupid of you, Hans. You ought to have led home the calf, and tied it to the manger."

"All right! I'll do better next time, mother."

When next time came,

"Where to, Hans?"

"To Grethel's, mother."

"Manage well, Hans."

"All right, mother! Good-bye."

"Good-bye, Hans."

Then Hans came to Grethel's.

"Good morning, Grethel."

"Good morning, Hans. What have you brought me to-day?"

"I have brought nothing, but I want to take away something."

Then Grethel said to Hans,

"You shall take away me."

Then Hans took Grethel, and tied a rope round her neck, and led her home, and fastened her up to the manger, and went to his mother.

"Good evening, mother."

"Good evening, Hans. Where have you been?"

"To Grethel's, mother."

"What did you take her, Hans?"

"Nothing, mother."

"What did Grethel give you, Hans?"

"Nothing but herself, mother."

"Where have you left Grethel, Hans?"

"I led her home with a rope, and tied her up to the manger to eat hay, mother."

"That was very stupid of you, Hans. You should have cast sheep's eyes at her."

"All right, mother! I'll do better next time."

Then Hans went into the stable, and taking all the eyes out of the sheep, he threw them in Grethel's face. Then Grethel was angry, and getting loose, she ran away and became the bride of another.

# Clever Else

There was once a man who had a daughter who was called "Clever Else," and when she was grown up, her father said she must be married, and her mother said,

"Yes, if we could only find some one that she would consent to have."

At last one came from a distance, and his name was Hans, and when he proposed to her, he made it a condition that clever Else should be very careful as well.

"Oh," said the father, "she does not want for brains."

"No, indeed," said the mother, "she can see the wind coming up the street and hear the flies cough."

"Well," said Hans, "if she does not turn out to be careful too, I will not have her."

Now when they were all seated at table, and had well eaten, the mother said,

"Else, go into the cellar and draw some beer."

Then Clever Else took down the jug from the hook in the

wall, and as she was on her way to the cellar she rattled the lid up and down so as to pass away the time. When she got there, she took a stool and stood it in front of the cask, so that she need not stoop and make her back ache with needless trouble. Then she put the jug under the tap and turned it, and while the beer was running, in order that her eyes should not be idle, she glanced hither and thither, and finally caught sight of a pickaxe that the workmen had left sticking in the ceiling just above her head. Then Clever Else began to cry, for she thought,

"If I marry Hans, and we have a child, and it grows big, and we send it into the cellar to draw beer, that pickaxe might fall on its head and kill it."

So there she sat and cried with all her might, lamenting the anticipated misfortune. All the while they were waiting upstairs for something to drink, and they waited in vain. At last the mistress said to the maid,

"Go down to the cellar and see why Else does not come."

So the maid went, and found her sitting in front of the cask crying with all her might.

"What are you crying for?" said the maid.

"Oh dear me," answered she, "how can I help crying? If I marry Hans, and we have a child, and it grows big, and we send it here to draw beer, perhaps the pickaxe may fall on its head and kill it."

"Our Else is clever indeed!" said the maid, and directly sat down to bewail the anticipated misfortune. After a while, when the people upstairs found that the maid did not return, and they were becoming more and more thirsty, the master said to the boy,

90

"You go down into the cellar, and see what Else and the maid are doing."

The boy did so, and there he found both Clever Else and the maid sitting crying together. Then he asked what was the matter.

"Oh dear me," said Else, "how can we help crying? If I marry Hans, and we have a child, and it grows big, and we send it here to draw beer, the pickaxe might fall on its head and kill it."

"Our Else is clever indeed!" said the boy, and sitting down beside her, he began howling with a good will. Upstairs they were all waiting for him to come back, but as he did not come, the master said to the mistress,

"You go down to the cellar and see what Else is doing."

So the mistress went down and found all three in great lamentations, and when she asked the cause, then Else told her how the future possible child might be killed as soon as it was big enough to be sent to draw beer, by the pickaxe falling on it. Then the mother at once exclaimed,

"Our Else is clever indeed!" and, sitting down, she wept with the rest.

Upstairs the husband waited a little while, but as his wife did not return, and as his thirst constantly increased, he said,

"I must go down to the cellar myself, and see what has become of Else." And when he came into the cellar, and found them all sitting and weeping together, he was told that it was all owing to the child that Else might possibly have, and the possibility of its being killed by the pickaxe so happening to

91

fall just at the time the child might be sitting underneath it drawing beer; and when he heard all this, he cried,

"How clever is our Else!" and sitting down, he joined his tears to theirs.

The intended bridegroom stayed upstairs by himself a long time, but as nobody came back to him, he thought he would go himself and see what they were all about. And there he found all five lamenting and crying most pitifully, each one louder than the other.

"What misfortune has happened?" cried he.

"O my dear Hans," said Else, "if we marry and have a child, and it grows big, and we send it down here to draw beer, perhaps that pickaxe which has been left sticking up there might fall down on the child's head and kill it; and how can we help crying at that!"

"Now," said Hans, "I cannot think that greater sense than that could be wanted in my household; so as you are so clever, Else, I will have you for my wife," and taking her by the hand he led her upstairs, and they had the wedding at once.

A little while after they were married, Hans said to his wife,

"I am going out to work, in order to get money; you go into the field and cut the corn, so that we may have bread."

"Very well, I will do so, dear Hans," said she. And after Hans was gone she cooked herself some nice stew, and took it with her into the field. And when she got there, she said to herself,

"Now, what shall I do? Shall I reap first, or eat first? All right, I will eat first." Then she ate her fill of stew, and when she could eat no more, she said to herself,

"Now, what shall I do? Shall I reap first, or sleep first? All right, I will sleep first." Then she lay down in the corn and went to sleep. And Hans got home, and waited there a long while, and Else did not come, so he said to himself,

"My clever Else is so industrious that she never thinks of coming home and eating."

But when evening drew near and still she did not come, Hans set out to see how much corn she had cut; but she had cut no corn at all, but there she was lying in it asleep. Then Hans made haste home, and fetched a bird-net with little bells and threw it over her; and still she went on sleeping. And he ran home again and locked himself in, and sat him down on his bench to work. At last, when it was beginning to grow dark, Clever Else woke, and when she got up and shook herself, the bells jingled at each movement that she made. Then she grew frightened, and began to doubt whether she were really Clever Else or not, and said to herself,

"Am I, or am I not?" And, not knowing what answer to make, she stood for a long while considering; at last she thought,

"I will go home to Hans and ask him if I am I or not; he is sure to know."

So she ran up to the door of her house, but it was locked; then she knocked at the window, and cried,

"Hans, is Else within?"

"Yes," answered Hans, "she is in."

Then she was in a greater fright than ever, and crying,

"Oh dear, then I am not I," she went to inquire at another door, but the people hearing the jingling of the bells would not open to her, and she could get in nowhere. So she ran away beyond the village, and since then no one has seen her.

# The Six Swans

Once on a time a king was hunting in a great wood, and he pursued a wild animal so eagerly that none of his people could follow him. When evening came he stood still, and looking round him he found that he had lost his way; and seeking a path, he found none. Then all at once he saw an old woman with a nodding head coming up to him; and it was a witch.

"My good woman," said he, "can you show me the way out of the wood?"

"Oh yes, my lord king," answered she, "certainly I can; but I must make a condition, and if you do not fulfil it, you will never get out of the wood again, but die there of hunger."

"What is the condition?" asked the king.

"I have a daughter," said the old woman, "who is as fair as any in the world, and if you will take her for your bride, and make her queen, I will show you the way out of the wood."

The king consented, because of the difficulty he was in, and the old woman led him into her little house, and there her daughter was sitting by the fire.

She received the king just as if she had been expecting him, and though he saw that she was very beautiful, she did not please him, and he could not look at her without an inward shudder. Nevertheless, he took the maiden before him on his horse, and the old woman showed him the way, and soon he was in his royal castle again, where the wedding was held.

The king had been married before, and his first wife had left seven children, six boys and one girl, whom he loved better than all the world, and as he was afraid the step-mother might not behave well to them, and perhaps would do them some mischief, he took them to a lonely castle standing in the middle of a wood. There they remained hidden, for the road to it was so hard to find that the king himself could not have found it, had it not been for a clew of yarn, possessing wonderful properties, that a wise woman had given him; when he threw it down before him, it unrolled itself and showed him the way. And the king went so often to see his dear children, that the queen was displeased at his absence; and she became curious and wanted to know what he went out into the wood for so often alone. She bribed his servants with much money, and they showed her the secret, and told her of the clew of yarn, which alone could point out the way; then she gave herself no rest until she had found out where the king kept the clew, and then she made some little white silk shirts, and sewed a charm in each, as she had learned witchcraft of her mother. And once when the king had ridden to the hunt, she took the little shirts and went into the wood, and the clew of yarn showed her the way. The children seeing some one in the distance, thought it was their dear father coming to see them, and came jumping for joy to meet him. Then the wicked queen threw over each one of the little shirts and as soon as the shirts touched their bodies, they were changed into swans, and flew away through the wood. So the queen went home very pleased to think she had got rid of her step-children; but the maiden had not run out with her brothers, and so the queen knew nothing about her. The next day the king went to see his children, but he found nobody but his daughter.

"Where are thy brothers?" asked the king.

"Ah, dear father," answered she, "they are gone away and have left me behind," and then she told him how she had seen from her window her brothers in the guise of swans fly away through the wood, and she showed him the feathers which they had let fall in the courtyard, and which she had picked up. The king was grieved, but he never dreamt that it was the queen who had done this wicked deed, and as he feared lest the maiden also should be stolen away from him, he wished to take her away with him. But she was afraid of the step-mother, and begged the king to let her remain one more night in the castle in the wood.

Then she said to herself,

"I must stay here no longer, but go and seek for my brothers."

And when the night came, she fled away and went straight into the wood. She went on all that night and the next day, until she could go no longer for weariness. At last she saw a rude hut, and she went in and found a room with six little beds in it; she did not dare to lie down in one, but she crept under one and lay on the hard boards and wished for night. When it was near the time of sun-setting she heard a rustling sound, and saw six swans come flying in at the window. They alighted on the ground, and blew at one another until they had blown all their feathers off, and then they stripped off their swan-skin as if it had been a shirt. And the maiden looked at them and knew them for her brothers, and was very glad, and crept from under the bed. The brothers were not less glad when their sister appeared, but their joy did not last long.

"You must not stay here," said they to her; "this is a robbers' haunt, and if they were to come and find you here, they would kill you."

"And cannot you defend me?" asked the little sister.

"No," answered they, "for we can only get rid of our swan-skins and keep our human shape every evening for a quarter of an hour, but after that we must be changed again into swans."

Their sister wept at hearing this, and said,

"Can nothing be done to set you free?"

"Oh no," answered they, "the work would be too hard for you. For six whole years you would be obliged never to speak or laugh, and make during that time six little shirts out of aster-flowers. If you were to let fall a single word before the work was ended, all would be of no good."

And just as the brothers had finished telling her this, the quarter of an hour came to an end, and they changed into swans and flew out of the window.

But the maiden made up her mind to set her brothers free, even though it should cost her her life. She left the hut, and going into the middle of the wood, she climbed a tree, and there passed the night. The next morning she set to work and gathered asters and began sewing them together: as for speaking, there was no one to speak to, and as for laughing, she had no mind to it; so she sat on and looked at nothing but her work. When she had been going on like this for a long time, it happened that the king of that country went a-hunting in the wood, and some of his huntsmen came up to the tree in which the maiden sat. They called out to her, saying, "Who art thou?" But she gave no answer. "Come down," cried they; "we will do thee no harm." But she only shook her head. And when they tormented her further with questions she threw down to them her gold necklace, hoping they would be content with that. But they would not leave off, so she threw down to them her girdle, and when that was no good, her garters, and one after another everything she had on and could possibly spare, until she had nothing left but her smock. But all was no good, the huntsmen would not be put off any longer, and they climbed the tree, carried the maiden off, and brought her to the king. The king asked, "Who art thou? What wert thou doing in the tree?" But she answered nothing. He spoke to her in all the languages he knew, but she remained dumb; but, being very beautiful, the king inclined to her, and he felt a great love rise up in his heart towards her; and casting his mantle round her, he put her before him on his horse and brought her to his castle. Then he caused rich clothing to be put upon her, and her beauty shone as bright as the morning, but no word would she utter. He seated her by his side at table, and her modesty and gentle mien so pleased him, that he said,

"This maiden I choose for wife, and no other in all the world," and accordingly after a few days they were married.

But the king had a wicked mother, who was displeased with the marriage, and spoke ill of the young queen.

"Who knows where the maid can have come from?" said she. "And not able to speak a word! She is not worthy of a king!"

After a year had passed, and the queen brought her first child into the world, the old woman carried it away, and marked the queen's mouth with blood as she lay sleeping. Then she went to the king and declared that his wife was an eater of human flesh. The king would not believe such a thing, and ordered that no one should do her any harm. And the queen went on quietly sewing the shirts and caring for nothing else. The next time that a fine boy was born, the wicked step-mother used the same deceit, but the king would give no credence to her words, for he said,

"She is too tender and good to do any such thing, and if she were only not dumb, and could justify herself, then her innocence would be as clear as day."

When for the third time the old woman stole away the new-born child and accused the queen, who was unable to say a word in her defence, the king could do no other but give her up to justice, and she was sentenced to suffer death by fire.

The day on which her sentence was to be carried out was the very last one of the sixth year of the years during which she had neither spoken nor laughed, to free her dear brothers from the evil spell. The six shirts were ready, all except one which wanted the left sleeve. And when she was led to the pile of wood, she carried the six shirts on her arm, and when she mounted the pile and the fire was about to be kindled, all at once she cried out aloud, for there were six swans coming flying through the air; and she saw that her deliverance was near, and her heart beat for joy. The swans came close up to her with rushing wings, and stooped round her, so that she could throw the shirts over them; and when that had been done the swanskins fell off them, and her brothers stood before her in their own bodies quite safe and sound; but as one shirt wanted the left sleeve, so the youngest brother had a swan's wing instead of a left arm. They embraced and kissed each other, and the queen went up to the king, who looked on full of astonishment, and began to speak to him and to say,

"Dearest husband, now I may dare to speak and tell you that I am innocent, and have been falsely accused," and she related to him the treachery of the step-mother, who had taken away the three children and hidden them. And she was reconciled to the king with great joy, and the wicked step-mother was bound to the stake on the pile of wood and burnt to ashes.

And the king and queen lived many years with their six brothers in peace and joy.

# The Rabbit's Bride

There was once a woman who lived with her daughter in a beautiful cabbage-garden; and there came a rabbit and ate up all the cabbages. At last said the woman to her daughter,

"Go into the garden, and drive out the rabbit."

"Shoo! Shoo!" said the maiden. "Don't eat up all our cabbages, little rabbit!"

"Come, maiden," said the rabbit, "sit on my tail and go with me to my rabbit-hutch." But the maiden would not.

Another day, back came the rabbit, and ate away at the cabbages, until the woman said to her daughter,

"Go into the garden, and drive away the rabbit."

"Shoo! Shoo!" said the maiden. "Don't eat up all our cabbages, little rabbit!"

"Come, maiden," said the rabbit, "sit on my tail and go with me to my rabbit-hutch." But the maiden would not.

103

Again, a third time back came the rabbit, and ate away at the cabbages, until the woman said to her daughter,

"Go into the garden, and drive away the rabbit."

"Shoo! Shoo!" said the maiden. "Don't eat up all our cabbages, little rabbit!"

"Come, maiden," said the rabbit, "sit on my tail and go with me to my rabbit-hutch."

And then the girl seated herself on the rabbit's tail, and the rabbit took her to his hutch.

"Now," said he, "set to work and cook some bran and cabbage; I am going to bid the wedding guests." And soon they were all collected. Would you like to know who they were? Well, I can only tell you what was told to me; all the hares came, and the crow who was to be the parson to marry them, and the fox for the clerk, and the altar was under the rainbow. But the maiden was sad, because she was so lonely.

"Get up! Get up!" said the rabbit. "The wedding folk are all merry."

But the bride wept and said nothing, and the rabbit went away, but very soon came back again.

"Get up! Get up!" said he. "The wedding folk are waiting." But the bride said nothing, and the rabbit went away. Then she made a figure of straw, and dressed it in her own clothes, and gave it a red mouth, and set it to watch the kettle of bran, and then she went home to her mother. Back again came the rabbit, saying, "Get up! Get up!" and he went up and hit the straw figure on the head, so that it tumbled down.

And the rabbit thought that he had killed his bride, and he went away and was very sad.

# King Thrushbeard

A king had a daughter, who was beautiful beyond measure, but so proud and overbearing that none of her suitors were good enough for her; she not only refused one after the other, but made a laughing-stock of them. Once the king appointed a great feast, and bade all the marriageable men to it from far and near. And they were all put in rows, according to their rank and station; first came the kings, then the princes, the dukes, the earls, the barons, and lastly the noblemen. The princess was led in front of the rows, but she had a mocking epithet for each. One was too fat, "What a tub!" said she. Another too tall, "Long and lean is ill to be seen," said she. A third too short, "Fat and short, not fit to court," said she. A fourth was too pale, "A regular death's-head"; a fifth too red-faced, "A gamecock," she called him. The sixth was not well-made enough, "Green wood ill dried!" cried she. So every one had something against him, and she made especially merry over a good king who was very tall, and whose chin had grown a little peaked.

"Only look," cried she, laughing, "he has a chin like a thrush's beak."

And from that time they called him King Thrushbeard. But the old king, when he saw that his daughter mocked every one, and scorned all the assembled suitors, swore in his anger that she should have the first beggar that came to the door for a husband.

A few days afterwards came a travelling ballad-singer, and sang under the window in hopes of a small alms. When the king heard of it, he said that he must come in. And so the ballad-singer entered in his dirty tattered garments, and sang before the king and his daughter; when he had done, he asked for a small reward. But the king said,

"Thy song has so well pleased me, that I will give thee my daughter to wife."

The princess was horrified; but the king said,

"I took an oath to give you to the first beggar that came, and so it must be done."

There was no remedy. The priest was fetched, and she had to be married to the ballad-singer out of hand. When all was done, the king said,

"Now, as you are a beggar-wife, you can stay no longer in my castle, so off with you and your husband."

The beggar-man led her away, and she was obliged to go forth with him on foot. On the way they came to a great wood, and she asked,

"Oh, whose is this forest, so thick and so fine?"

He answered,

"It is King Thrushbeard's, and might have been thine."

And she cried,

"Oh, I was a silly young thing, I'm afeared,
  Would I had taken that good King Thrushbeard!"

Then they passed through a meadow, and she asked,

"Oh, whose is this meadow, so green and so fine?"

He answered,

"It is King Thrushbeard's, and might have been thine."

And she cried,

"I was a silly young thing, I'm afeared,
  Would I had taken that good King Thrushbeard!"

Then they passed through a great town, and she asked,

"Whose is this city, so great and so fine?"

He answered,

"Oh, it is King Thrushbeard's, and might have been thine."

And she cried,

"I was a silly young thing, I'm afeared,
  Would I had taken that good King Thrushbeard!"

Then said the beggar-man,

107

"It does not please me to hear you always wishing for another husband. Am I not good enough for you?"

At last they came to a very small house, and she said,

"Oh, dear me! What poor little house do I see?
And whose, I would know, may the wretched hole be?"

The man answered,
"That is my house and thine, where we must live together."
She had to stoop before she could go in at the door.

"Where are the servants?" asked the king's daughter.

"What servants?" answered the beggar-man. "What you want to have done you must do yourself. Make a fire quick, and put on water, and cook me some food; I am very tired."

But the king's daughter understood nothing about fire-making and cooking, and the beggar-man had to lend a hand himself in order to manage it at all. And when they had eaten their poor fare, they went to bed; but the man called up his wife very early in the morning, in order to clean the house. For a few days they lived in this indifferent manner, until they came to the end of their store.

"Wife," said the man, "this will not do, stopping here and earning nothing; you must make baskets."

So he went out and cut willows, and brought them home; and she began to weave them, but the hard twigs wounded her tender hands.

"I see this will not do," said the man, "you had better try spinning."

So she sat her down and tried to spin, but the harsh thread cut her soft fingers, so that the blood flowed.

"Look now!" said the man. "You are no good at any sort of work; I made a bad bargain when I took you. I must see what I can do to make a trade of pots and earthen vessels; you can sit in the market and offer them for sale."

"Oh dear!" thought she. "Suppose while I am selling in the market people belonging to my father's kingdom should see me, how they would mock at me!"

But there was no help for it; she had to submit, or else die of hunger.

The first day all went well; the people bought her wares eagerly, because she was so beautiful, and gave her whatever she asked, and some of them gave her the money and left the pots after all behind them. And they lived on these earnings as long as they lasted; and then the man bought a number of new pots. So she seated herself in a corner of the market, and stood the wares before her for sale. All at once a drunken horse-soldier came plunging by, and rode straight into the midst of her pots, breaking them into a thousand pieces. She could do nothing for weeping.

"Oh dear, what will become of me," cried she; "what will my husband say?" and she hastened home and told him her misfortune.

"Who ever heard of such a thing as sitting in the corner of the market with earthenware pots!" said the man. "Now leave off crying; I see you are not fit for any regular work. I have been asking at your father's castle if they want a kitchen-maid, and they say they don't mind taking you; at any rate you will get your victuals free."

And the king's daughter became a kitchen-maid, to be at the

cook's beck and call, and do the hardest work. In each of her pockets she fastened a little pot, and brought home in them whatever was left, and upon that she and her husband were fed. It happened one day, when the wedding of the eldest prince was celebrated, the poor woman went upstairs, and stood by the parlour door to see what was going on. And when the place was lighted up, and the company arrived, each person handsomer than the one before, and all was brilliancy and splendour, she thought of her own fate with a sad heart, and bewailed her former pride and haughtiness which had brought her so low, and plunged her in so great poverty. And as the rich and delicate dishes smelling so good were carried to and fro every now and then, the servants would throw her a few fragments which she put in her pockets, intending to take home. And then the prince himself passed in clothed in silk and velvet, with a gold chain around his neck. And when he saw the beautiful woman standing in the doorway, he seized her hand and urged her to dance with him, but she refused, all trembling, for she saw it was King Thrushbeard, who had come to court her, whom she had turned away with mocking. It was of no use her resisting, he drew her into the room; and all at once the band to which her pockets were fastened broke, and the pots fell out, and the soup ran about, and the fragments were scattered all round. And when the people saw that, there was great laughter and mocking, and she felt so ashamed, that she wished herself a thousand fathoms underground. She rushed to the door to fly from the place, when a man caught her just on the steps, and when she looked at him, it was King Thrushbeard again. He said to her in a kind tone,

"Do not be afraid, I and the beggar-man with whom you lived in the wretched little hut are one. For love of you, I disguised myself, and it was I who broke your pots in the guise of a horse-soldier. I did all that to bring down your proud heart, and to punish your haughtiness, which caused you to mock at me." Then she wept bitterly, and said,

"I have done great wrong, and am not worthy to be your wife."

But he said,

"Take courage, the evil days are gone over; now let us keep our wedding-day."

Then came the ladies-in-waiting and put on her splendid clothing; and her father came, and the whole court, and wished her joy on her marriage with King Thrushbeard; and then the merry-making began in good earnest. I cannot help wishing that you and I could have been there too.

# Tom Thumb

There was once a poor countryman who used to sit in the chimney-corner all evening and poke the fire, while his wife sat at her spinning-wheel.

And he used to say,

"How dull it is without any children about us; our house is so quiet, and other people's houses so noisy and merry!"

"Yes!" answered his wife, and sighed. "If we could only have one, and that one ever so little, no bigger than my thumb, how happy I should be! It would, indeed, be having our hearts' desire."

Now, it happened that after a while the woman had a child who was perfect in all his limbs, but no bigger than a thumb. Then the parents said,

"He is just what we wished for, and we will love him very much," and they named him according to his stature, "Tom

Thumb." And though they gave him plenty of nourishment, he grew no bigger, but remained exactly the same size as when he was first born; and he had very good faculties, and was very quick and prudent, so that all he did prospered.

One day his father made ready to go into the forest to cut wood, and he said, as if to himself,

"Now, I wish there was some one to bring the cart to meet me."

"O father," cried Tom Thumb, "I can bring the cart, let me alone for that, and in proper time, too!"

Then the father laughed, and said,

"How will you manage that? You are much too little to hold the reins."

"That has nothing to do with it, father; while my mother goes on with her spinning I will sit in the horse's ear and tell him where to go."

"Well," answered the father, "we will try it for once."

When it was time to set off, the mother went on spinning, after setting Tom Thumb in the horse's ear; and so he drove off, crying,

"Gee-up, gee-wo!"

So the horse went on quite as if his master were driving him, and drew the waggon along the right road to the wood.

Now it happened just as they turned a corner, and the little fellow was calling out "Gee-up!" that two strange men passed by.

"Look," said one of them, "how is this? There goes a waggon and the driver is calling to the horse, and yet he is nowhere to be seen."

114

"It is very strange," said the other; "we will follow the wag-gon, and see where it belongs."

And the waggon went right through the wood, up to the place where the wood had been hewed. When Tom Thumb caught sight of his father, he cried out,

"Look, father, here am I with the waggon; now, take me down."

The father held the horse with his left hand, and with the right he lifted down his little son out of the horse's ear, and Tom Thumb sat down on a stump, quite happy and content. When the two strangers saw him they were struck dumb with wonder. At last one of them, taking the other aside, said to him, "Look here, the little chap would make our fortune if we were to show him in the town for money. Suppose we buy him."

So they went up to the woodcutter, and said,

"Sell the little man to us; we will take care he shall come to no harm."

"No," answered the father. "He is the apple of my eye, and not for all the money in the world would I sell him."

But Tom Thumb, when he heard what was going on, climbed up by his father's coat tails, and, perching himself on his shoulder, he whispered in his ear,

"Father, you might as well let me go. I will soon come back again."

Then the father gave him up to the two men for a large piece of money. They asked him where he would like to sit,

"Oh, put me on the brim of your hat," said he. "There I can

115

walk about and view the country, and be in no danger of falling off."

So they did as he wished, and when Tom Thumb had taken leave of his father, they set off all together. And they travelled on until it grew dusk, and the little fellow asked to be set down a little while for a change, and after some difficulty they consented. So the man took him down from his hat, and set him in a field by the roadside, and he ran away directly, and, after creeping about among the furrows, he slipped suddenly into a mouse-hole, just what he was looking for.

"Good evening, my masters, you can go home without me!" cried he to them, laughing. They ran up and felt about with their sticks in the mouse-hole, but in vain. Tom Thumb crept farther and farther in, and as it was growing dark, they had to make the best of their way home, full of vexation, and with empty purses.

When Tom Thumb found they were gone, he crept out of his hiding-place underground.

"It is dangerous work groping about these holes in the darkness," said he; "I might easily break my neck."

But by good fortune he came upon an empty snail shell.

"That's all right," said he. "Now I can get safely through the night"; and he settled himself down in it. Before he had time to get to sleep, he heard two men pass by, and one was saying to the other,

"How can we manage to get hold of the rich parson's gold and silver?"

"I can tell you how," cried Tom Thumb.

116

"How is this?" said one of the thieves, quite frightened, "I hear some one speak!"

So they stood still and listened, and Tom Thumb spoke again.

"Take me with you; I will show you how to do it!"

"Where are you, then?" asked they.

"Look about on the ground and notice where the voice comes from," answered he.

At last they found him, and lifted him up.

"You little elf," said they, "how can you help us?"

"Look here," answered he, "I can easily creep between the iron bars of the parson's room and hand out to you whatever you would like to have."

"Very well," said they, "we will try what you can do."

So when they came to the parsonage-house, Tom Thumb crept into the room, but cried out with all his might,

"Will you have all that is here?" So the thieves were terrified, and said,

"Do speak more softly, lest any one should be awaked."

But Tom Thumb made as if he did not hear them, and cried out again,

"What would you like? Will you have all that is here?" so that the cook, who was sleeping in a room hard by, heard it, and raised herself in bed and listened. The thieves, however, in their fear of being discovered, had run back part of the way, but they took courage again, thinking that it was only a jest of the little fellow's. So they came back and whispered to him to be serious, and to hand them out something.

Then Tom Thumb called out once more as loud as he could,

"Oh yes, I will give it all to you, only put out your hands."

Then the listening maid heard him distinctly that time, and jumped out of bed, and burst open the door. The thieves ran off as if the wild huntsman were behind them; but the maid, as she could see nothing, went to fetch a light. And when she came back with one, Tom Thumb had taken himself off, without being seen by her, into the barn; and the maid, when she had looked in every hole and corner and found nothing, went back to bed at last, and thought that she must have been dreaming with her eyes and ears open.

So Tom Thumb crept among the hay, and found a comfortable nook to sleep in, where he intended to remain until it was day, and then to go home to his father and mother. But other things were to befall him; indeed there is nothing but trouble and worry in this world! The maid got up at dawn of day to feed the cows. The first place she went to was the barn, where she took up an armful of hay, and it happened to be the very heap in which Tom Thumb lay asleep. And he was so fast asleep, that he was aware of nothing, and never waked until he was in the mouth of the cow, who had taken him up with the hay.

"Oh dear," cried he, "how is it that I have got into a mill!" but he soon found out where he was, and he had to be very careful not to get between the cow's teeth, and at last he had to descend into the cow's stomach.

"The windows were forgotten when this little room was built," said he, "and the sunshine cannot get in; there is no light to be had."

His quarters were in every way unpleasant to him, and, what

was the worst, new hay was constantly coming in, and the space
was being filled up. At last he cried out in his extremity, as loud
as he could,

"No more hay for me! No more hay for me!'

The maid was then milking the cow, and as she heard a
voice, but could see no one, and as it was the same voice that
she had heard in the night, she was so frightened that she fell
off her stool, and spilt the milk. Then she ran in great haste to
her master, crying,

"Oh, master dear, the cow spoke!"

"You must be crazy," answered her master, and he went
himself to the cow-house to see what was the matter. No sooner
had he put his foot inside the door, than Tom Thumb cried
out again,

"No more hay for me! No more hay for me!"

Then the parson himself was frightened, supposing that a
bad spirit had entered the cow, and he ordered her to be put to
death. So she was killed, but the stomach, where Tom Thumb
was lying, was thrown upon a dunghill. Tom Thumb had great
trouble to work his way out of it, and he had just made a space
big enough for his head to go through, when a great misfortune
happened. A hungry wolf ran up and swallowed the whole stomach at one gulp. But Tom Thumb did not lose courage. "Perhaps," thought he, "the wolf will listen to reason," and he
cried from the inside of the wolf,

"My dear wolf, I can tell you where to get a splendid meal!"

"Where is it to be had?" asked the wolf.

"In such and such a house, and you must creep into it
through the drain, and there you will find cakes and bacon and

broth, as much as you can eat," and he described to him his father's house. The wolf needed not to be told twice. He squeezed himself through the drain in the night, and feasted in the store-room to his heart's content. When, at last, he was satisfied, he wanted to go away again, but he had become so big, that to creep the same way back was impossible. This Tom Thumb had reckoned upon, and began to make a terrible din inside the wolf, crying and calling as loud as he could.

"Will you be quiet?" said the wolf. "You will wake the folks up!"

"Look here," cried the little man, "you are very well satisfied, and now I will do something for my own enjoyment," and began again to make all the noise he could. At last the father and mother were awakened, and they ran to the room-door and peeped through the chink, and when they saw a wolf in occupation, they ran and fetched weapons—the man an axe, and the wife a scythe.

"Stay behind," said the man, as they entered the room; "when I have given him a blow, and it does not seem to have killed him, then you must cut at him with your scythe."

Then Tom Thumb heard his father's voice, and cried,

"Dear father, I am here in the wolf's inside."

Then the father called out full of joy,

"Thank heaven that we have found our dear child!" and told his wife to keep the scythe out of the way, lest Tom Thumb should be hurt with it. Then he drew near and struck the wolf such a blow on the head that he fell down dead; and then he fetched a knife and a pair of scissors, slit up the wolf's body, and let out the little fellow.

120

"Oh, what anxiety we have felt about you!" said the father.

"Yes, father, I have seen a good deal of the world, and I am very glad to breathe fresh air again."

"And where have you been all this time?" asked his father.

"Oh, I have been in a mouse-hole and a snail's shell, in a cow's stomach and a wolf's inside: now, I think, I will stay at home."

"And we will not part with you for all the kingdoms of the world," cried the parents, as they kissed and hugged their dear little Tom Thumb. And they gave him something to eat and drink, and a new suit of clothes, as his old ones were soiled with travel.

# Tom Thumb's Travels

There was once a tailor who had a son no higher than a thumb, so he was called Tom Thumb. Notwithstanding his small size, he had plenty of spirit, and one day he said to his father,

"Father, go out into the world I must and will."

"Very well, my son," said the old man, and taking a long darning needle, he put a knob of sealing-wax on the end, saying,

"Here is a sword to take with you on your journey."

Now the little tailor wanted to have one more meal first, and so he trotted into the kitchen to see what sort of a farewell feast his mother had cooked for him. It was all ready, and the dish was standing on the hearth. Then said he,

"Mother, what is the fare to-day?"

"You can see for yourself," said the mother. Then Tom Thumb ran to the hearth and peeped into the dish, but as he stretched his neck too far over it, the steam caught him and carried him up the chimney. For a time he floated with the steam about in the air, but at last he sank down to the ground. Then the little tailor found himself out in the wide world, and he wandered about, and finally engaged himself to a master tailor, but the food was not good enough for him.

"Mistress," said Tom Thumb, "if you do not give us better victuals, I shall go out early in the morning and write with a piece of chalk on the house-door, 'Plenty of potatoes to eat, and but little meat; so good-bye, Mr. Potato.'"

"What are you after, grasshopper?" said the mistress, and growing angry she seized a piece of rag to beat him off; but he crept underneath her thimble, and then peeped at her, and put his tongue out at her. She took up the thimble, and would have seized him, but he hopped among the rags, and as the mistress turned them over to find him, he stepped into a crack in the table. "He-hee! Mistress!" cried he, sticking out his head, and when she was just going to grasp him, he jumped into the table-drawer. But in the end she caught him, and drove him out of the house.

So he wandered on until he came to a great wood; and there he met a gang of robbers that were going to rob the king's treasury. When they saw the little tailor, they thought to themselves,

"Such a little fellow might easily creep through a key-hole, and serve instead of a pick-lock."

"Holloa!" cried one. "You giant Goliath, will you come with us to the treasure-chamber? You can slip in, and then throw us out the money."

Tom Thumb considered a little, but at last he consented

and went with them to the treasure-chamber. Then he looked all over the doors above and below, but there was no crack to be seen; at last he found one broad enough to let him pass, and he was getting through, when one of the sentinels that stood before the door saw him, and said to the other,

"See what an ugly spider is crawling there! I will put an end to him."

"Let the poor creature alone," said the other, "it has done you no harm."

So Tom Thumb got safely through the crack into the treasure-chamber, and he opened the window beneath which the thieves were standing, and he threw out one dollar after another. Just as he had well settled to the work, he heard the king coming to take a look at his treasure, and so Tom Thumb had to creep away. The king presently remarked that many good dollars were wanting, but could not imagine how they could have been stolen, as the locks and bolts were in good order, and everything seemed secure. And he went away, saying to the two sentinels,

"Keep good guard; there is some one after the money."

When Tom Thumb had set to work anew, they heard the chink, chink of the money, and hastily rushed in to catch the thief. But the little tailor, as he heard them coming, was too quick for them, and, hiding in a corner, he covered himself up with a dollar, so that nothing of him was to be seen, and then he mocked the sentinels, crying, "Here I am!" They ran about, and when they came near him, he was soon in another corner under a dollar, crying, "Here I am!" Then the sentinels ran towards him, and in a moment he was in a third corner, crying,

125

"Here I am!" In this way he made fools of them, and dodged them so long about the treasure-chamber, that they got tired and went away. Then he set to work, and threw the dollars out of the window, one after the other, till they were all gone; and when it came to the last, as he flung it with all his might, he jumped nimbly on it, and flew with it out of the window. The robbers gave him great praise, saying,

"You are a most valiant hero; will you be our captain?"

But Tom Thumb thanked them, and said he would like to see the world first. Then they divided the spoil; but the little tailor's share was only one farthing, which was all he was able to carry.

Then binding his sword to his side, he bid the robbers good day, and started on his way. He applied to several master tailors, but they would not have anything to do with him; and at last he hired himself as indoor servant at an inn. The maid servants took a great dislike to him, for he used to see everything they did without being seen by them, and he told the master and mistress about what they took from the plates, and what they carried away out of the cellar. And they said, "Wait a little, we will pay you out," and took counsel together to play him some mischievous trick. Once when one of the maids was mowing the grass in the garden she saw Tom Thumb jumping about and creeping among the cabbages, and she mowed him with the grass, tied all together in a bundle, and threw it to the cows. Among the cows was a big black one, who swallowed him down, without doing him any harm. But he did not like his lodging, it was so dark, and there was no candle to be had. When the cow was being milked, he cried out,

126

"Strip, strap, strull,
 Will the pail soon be full?"

But he was not understood because of the noise of the milk. Presently the landlord came into the stable and said,

"To-morrow this cow is to be slaughtered."

At that Tom Thumb felt very terrified; and with his shrillest voice he cried,

"Let me out first; I am sitting inside here!"

The master heard him quite plainly, but could not tell where the voice came from.

"Where are you?" asked he.

"Inside the black one," answered Tom Thumb, but the master, not understanding the meaning of it all, went away.

The next morning the cow was slaughtered. Happily, in all the cutting and slashing he escaped all harm, and he slipped among the sausage-meat. When the butcher came near to set to work, he cried with all his might,

"Don't cut so deep, don't cut so deep, I am underneath!"

But for the sound of the butcher's knife his voice was not heard. Now, poor Tom Thumb was in great straits, and he had to jump nimbly out of the way of the knife, and finally he came through with a whole skin. But he could not get quite away, and he had to let himself remain with the lumps of fat to be put in a black pudding. His quarters were rather narrow, and he had to be hung up in the chimney in the smoke, and to remain there a very long while. At last, when winter came he was taken down, for the black pudding was to be set before a guest. And when the landlady cut the black pudding in slices,

127

he had to take great care not to lift up his head too much, or it might be shaved off at the neck. At last he saw his opportunity, took courage, and jumped out.

But as things had gone so badly with him in that house, Tom Thumb did not mean to stay there, but betook himself again to his wanderings. His freedom, however, did not last long. In the open fields there came a fox who snapped him up without thinking.

"Oh, Mr. Fox," cried Tom Thumb, "here I am sticking in your throat; let me out again."

"Very well," answered the fox. "It is true you are no better than nothing; promise me the hens in your father's yard, then I will let you go."

"With all my heart," answered Tom Thumb, "you shall have them all, I promise you."

Then the fox let him go, and he ran home. When the father saw his dear little son again, he gave the fox willingly all the hens that he had.

"And look, besides, what a fine piece of money I've got for you!" said Tom Thumb, and handed over the farthing which he had earned in his wanderings.

But how, you ask, could they let the fox devour all the poor chicks?

Why, you silly child, you know that your father would rather have you than the hens in his yard!

# Six Soldiers of Fortune

There was once a man who was a Jack-of-all-trades; he had served in the war, and had been brave and bold, but at the end of it he was sent about his business, with three farthings and his discharge.

"I am not going to stand this," said he. "Wait till I find the right man to help me, and the king shall give me all the treasures of his kingdom before he has done with me."

Then, full of wrath, he went into the forest, and he saw one standing there by six trees which he had rooted up as if they had been stalks of corn. And he said to him,

"Will you be my man, and come along with me?"

"All right," answered he. "I must just take this bit of wood home to my father and mother." And taking one of the trees, he bound it round the other five, and putting the faggot on his shoulder, he carried it off; then soon coming back, he went along with his leader, who said,

"Two such as we can stand against the whole world."

And when they had gone on a little while, they came to a huntsman who was kneeling on one knee and taking careful aim with his rifle.

"Huntsman," said the leader, "what are you aiming at?"

"Two miles from here," answered he, "there sits a fly on the bough of an oak-tree. I mean to put a bullet into its left eye."

"Oh, come along with me," said the leader. "Three of us together can stand against the world."

The huntsman was quite willing to go with him, and so they went on till they came to seven windmills, whose sails were going round briskly, and yet there was no wind blowing from any quarter, and not a leaf stirred.

"Well," said the leader, "I cannot think what ails the windmills, turning without wind;" and he went on with his followers about two miles farther, and then they came to a man sitting up in a tree, holding one nostril and blowing with the other.

"Now then," said the leader, "what are you doing up there?"

"Two miles from here," answered he, "there are seven windmills. I am blowing, and they are going round."

"Oh, go with me," cried the leader. "Four of us together can stand against the world."

So the blower got down and went with them, and after a time they came to a man standing on one leg, and the other had been taken off and was lying near him.

"You seem to have got a handy way of resting yourself," said the leader to the man.

"I am a runner," answered he, "and in order to keep myself from going too fast I have taken off a leg, for when I run with both, I go faster than a bird can fly."

"Oh, go with me," cried the leader. "Five of us together may well stand against the world."

So he went with them all together, and it was not long before they met a man with a little hat on, and he wore it just over one ear.

"Manners! Manners!" said the leader. "With your hat like that, you look like a jack-fool."

"I dare not put it straight," answered the other; "if I did, there would be such a terrible frost that the very birds would be frozen and fall dead from the sky to the ground."

"Oh, come with me," said the leader. "We six together may well stand against the whole world."

So the six went on until they came to a town where the king had caused it to be made known that whoever would run a race with his daughter and win it might become her husband, but that whoever lost must lose his head into the bargain. And the leader came forward and said one of his men should run for him.

"Then," said the king, "his life too must be put in pledge, and if he fails, his head and yours too must fall."

When this was quite settled and agreed upon, the leader called the runner, and strapped his second leg on to him.

"Now, look out," said he, "and take care that we win."

It had been agreed that the one who should bring water first from a far distant brook should be accounted winner. Now the king's daughter and the runner each took a pitcher, and they started both at the same time; but in one moment, when the king's daughter had gone but a very little way, the runner was out of sight, for his running was as if the wind rushed by. In a short time he reached the brook, filled his pitcher full of water, and turned back again. About half-way home, however, he was overcome with weariness, and setting down his pitcher, he lay down on the ground to sleep. But in order to awaken soon again by not lying too soft he had taken a horse's skull which lay near and placed it under his head for a pillow. In the meanwhile the king's daughter, who really was a good runner, good enough to beat an ordinary man, had reached the brook, and filled her pitcher, and was hastening with it back again, when she saw the runner lying asleep.

"The day is mine," said she with much joy, and she emptied his pitcher and hastened on. And now all had been lost but for the huntsman who was standing on the castle wall, and with his keen eyes saw all that happened.

"We must not be outdone by the king's daughter," said he, and he loaded his rifle and took so good an aim that he shot the horse's skull from under the runner's head without doing him any harm. And the runner awoke and jumped up, and saw his pitcher standing empty and the king's daughter far on her way home. But, not losing courage, he ran swiftly to the brook, filled it again with water, and for all that, he got home ten minutes before the king's daughter.

"Look you," said he; "this is the first time I have really stretched my legs; before it was not worth the name of running."

The king was vexed, and his daughter yet more so, that she

132

should be beaten by a discharged common soldier; and they took counsel together how they might rid themselves of him and of his companions at the same time.

"I have a plan," said the king; "do not fear but that we shall be quit of them forever." Then he went out to the men and bade them to feast and be merry and eat and drink; and he led them into a room, which had a floor of iron, and the doors were iron, the windows had iron frames and bolts; in the room was a table set out with costly food.

"Now, go in there and make yourselves comfortable," said the king.

And when they had gone in, he had the door locked and bolted. Then he called the cook, and told him to make a big fire underneath the room, so that the iron floor of it should be red hot. And the cook did so, and the six men began to feel the room growing very warm, by reason, as they thought at first, of the good dinner; but as the heat grew greater and greater, and they found the doors and windows fastened, they began to think it was an evil plan of the king's to suffocate them.

"He shall not succeed, however," said the man with the little hat. "I will bring on a frost that shall make the fire feel ashamed of itself, and creep out of the way."

So he set his hat straight on his head, and immediately there came such a frost that all the heat passed away and the food froze in the dishes. After an hour or two had passed, and the king thought they must have all perished in the heat, he caused the door to be opened, and went himself to see how they fared. And when the door flew back, there they were all six quite safe and sound, and they said they were quite ready to come out, so that they might warm themselves, for the great cold of that room had caused the food to freeze in the dishes. Full of wrath, the king went to the cook and scolded him, and asked why he had not done as he was ordered.

"It is hot enough there: you may see for yourself," answered the cook. And the king looked and saw an immense fire burning underneath the room of iron, and he began to think that the six men were not to be got rid of in that way. And he thought of a new plan by which it might be managed, so he sent for the leader and said to him,

"If you will give up your right to my daughter, and take gold instead, you may have as much as you like."

"Certainly, my lord king," answered the man. "Let me have as much gold as my servant can carry, and I give up all claim to your daughter." And the king agreed that he should come again in a fortnight to fetch the gold. The man then called together all the tailors in the kingdom, and set them to work to make a sack, and it took them a fortnight. And when it was ready, the strong man who had been found rooting up trees took it on his shoulder, and went to the king.

"Who is this immense fellow carrying on his shoulder a bundle of stuff as big as a house?" cried the king, terrified to think how much gold he would carry off. And a ton of gold was dragged in by sixteen strong men, but he put it all into the sack with one hand, saying,

"Why don't you bring some more? This hardly covers the bottom!" So the king bade them fetch by degrees the whole of his treasure, and even then the sack was not half full.

"Bring more!" cried the man. "These few scraps go no way

at all!" Then at last seven thousand waggons laden with gold collected through the whole kingdom were driven up; and he threw them in his sack, oxen and all.

"I will not look too closely," said he, "but take what I can get, so long as the sack is full." And when all was put in there was still plenty of room.

"I must make an end of this," he said. "If it is not full, it is so much the easier to tie up." And he hoisted it on his back, and went off with his comrades.

When the king saw all the wealth of his realm carried off by a single man he was full of wrath, and he bade his cavalry mount, and follow after the six men, and take the sack away from the strong man.

Two regiments were soon up to them, and called them to consider themselves prisoners, and to deliver up the sack, or be cut in pieces.

"Prisoners, say you?" said the man who could blow. "Suppose you first have a little dance together in the air," and holding one nostril, and blowing through the other, he sent the regiments flying head over heels, over the hills and far away. But a sergeant who had nine wounds and was a brave fellow, begged not to be put to so much shame. And the blower let him down easily, so that he came to no harm, and he bade him go to the king and tell him that whatever regiments he liked to send more should be blown away just the same. And the king, when he got the message, said,

"Let the fellows be; they have some right on their side." So the six comrades carried home their treasure, divided it among them, and lived contented till they died.

# Clever Grethel

There was once a cook called Grethel, who wore shoes with red heels, and when she went out in them she gave herself great airs, and thought herself very fine indeed. When she came home again, she would take a drink of wine to refresh herself, and as that gave her an appetite, she would take some of the best of whatever she was cooking, until she had had enough; "for," said she, "a cook must know how things taste."

Now it happened that one day her master said to her,

"Grethel, I expect a guest this evening. You must make ready a pair of fowls."

"Certainly, sir, I will," answered Grethel. So she killed the fowls, cleaned them, and plucked them, and put them on the spit, and then, as evening drew near, placed them before the fire to roast. And they began to be brown, and were nearly done, but the guest had not come.

"If he does not make haste," cried Grethel to her master, "I must take them away from the fire; it's a pity and a shame not to eat them now, just when they are done to a turn." And the master said he would run himself and fetch the guest. As soon as he had turned his back, Grethel took the fowls from before the fire.

"Standing so long before the fire," said she, "makes one hot and thirsty—and who knows when they will come! In the meanwhile I will go to the cellar and have a drink." So down she ran, took up a mug, and saying, "Here's to me!" took a good draught. "One good drink deserves another," she said, "and it should not be cut short;" so she took another hearty draught. Then she went and put the fowls down to the fire again, and, basting them with butter, she turned the spit briskly round. And now they began to smell so good that Grethel saying, "I must find out whether they really are all right," licked her fingers, and then cried, "Well, I never! The fowls are good; it's a sin and a shame that no one is here to eat them!"

So she ran to the window to see if her master and his guest were coming, but as she could see nobody she went back to her fowls. "Why, one of the wings is burning!" she cried presently. "I had better eat it and get it out of the way." So she cut it off and ate it up, and it tasted good, and then she thought,

"I had better cut off the other too, in case the master should miss anything." And when both wings had been disposed of she went and looked for the master, but still he did not come.

"Who knows," said she, "whether they are coming or not? They may have put up at an inn." And after a pause she said again, "Come, I may as well make myself happy, and first I

will make sure of a good drink and then of a good meal, and
when all is done I shall be easy; the gifts of the gods are not
to be despised." So first she ran down into the cellar and had
a famous drink, and ate up one of the fowls with great relish.
And when that was done, and still the master did not come,
Grethel eyed the other fowl, saying, "What one is, the other
must be, the two belong to each other, it is only fair that they
should be both treated alike; perhaps, when I have had another
drink, I shall be able to manage it." So she took another hearty
drink, and then the second fowl went the way of the first.

Just as she was in the middle of it the master came back.
"Make haste, Grethel," cried he. "The guest is coming directly!" "Very well, master," she answered. "It will soon be
ready." The master went to see that the table was properly
laid, and, taking the great carving knife with which he meant
to carve the fowls, he sharpened it upon the step. Presently
came the guest, knocking very genteelly and softly at the front
door. Grethel ran and looked to see who it was, and when she
caught sight of the guest she put her finger on her lip saying,
"Hush! Make the best haste you can out of this, for if my
master catches you, it will be bad for you; he asked you to come
to supper, but he really means to cut off your ears! Just listen
how he is sharpening his knife!"

The guest, hearing the noise of the sharpening, made off as
fast as he could go. And Grethel ran screaming to her master.
"A pretty guest you have asked to the house!" cried she.

"How so, Grethel? What do you mean?" asked he.

"What indeed!" said she. "Why, he has gone and run away
with my pair of fowls that I had just dished up."

"That's pretty sort of conduct!" said the master, feeling very sorry about the fowls. "He might at least have left me one, that I might have had something to eat." And he called out to him to stop, but the guest made as if he did not hear him; then he ran after him, the knife still in his hand, crying out, "Only one! Only one!" meaning that the guest should let him have one of the fowls and not take both, but the guest thought he meant to have only one of his ears, and he ran so much the faster that he might get home with both of them safe.

# The Fisherman and
# his Wife

There was once a fisherman and his wife who lived together in
a hovel by the sea-shore, and the fisherman went out every day
with his hook and line to catch fish, and he angled and angled.

One day he was sitting with his rod and looking into the clear
water, and he sat and sat.

At last down went the line to the bottom of the water, and
when he drew it up he found a great flounder on the hook. And
the flounder said to him,

"Fisherman, listen to me; let me go, I am not a real fish but
an enchanted prince. What good shall I be to you if you land
me? I shall not taste well; so put me back into the water again,
and let me swim away."

"Well," said the fisherman, "no need of so many words about
the matter, as you can speak I had much rather let you swim
away."

Then he put him back into the clear water, and the flounder
sank to the bottom, leaving a long streak of blood behind him.
Then the fisherman got up and went home to his wife in their
hovel.

"Well, husband," said the wife, "have you caught nothing
to-day?"

"No," said the man—"that is, I did catch a flounder, but as he
said he was an enchanted prince, I let him go again."

"Then, did you wish for nothing?" said the wife.

"No," said the man; "what should I wish for?"

"Oh dear!" said the wife; "and it is so dreadful always to live
in this evil-smelling hovel; you might as well have wished for a
little cottage; go again and call him; tell him we want a little
cottage, I daresay he will give it us; go, and be quick."

And when he went back, the sea was green and yellow, and
not nearly so clear. So he stood and said,

"O man, O man!—if man you be,
  Or flounder, flounder, in the sea—
  Such a tiresome wife I've got,
  For she wants what I do not."

Then the flounder came swimming up, and said,

"Now then, what does she want?"

"Oh," said the man, "you know when I caught you my wife
says I ought to have wished for something. She does not want
to live any longer in the hovel, and would rather have a cottage."

"Go home with you," said the flounder. "She has it already."

142

So the man went home, and found, instead of the hovel, a little cottage, and his wife was sitting on a bench before the door. And she took him by the hand, and said to him,

"Come in and see if this is not a great improvement."

So they went in, and there was a little house-place and a beautiful little bedroom, a kitchen and larder, with all sorts of furniture, and iron and brass ware of the very best. And at the back was a little yard with fowls and ducks, and a little garden full of green vegetables and fruit.

"Look," said the wife, "is not that nice?"

"Yes," said the man, "if this can only last we shall be very well contented."

"We will see about that," said the wife. And after a meal they went to bed.

So all went well for a week or fortnight, when the wife said,

"Look here, husband, the cottage is really too confined, and the yard and garden are so small; I think the flounder had better get us a larger house; I should like very much to live in a large stone castle; so go to your fish and he will send us a castle."

"O my dear wife," said the man, "the cottage is good enough; what do we want a castle for?"

"We want one," said the wife. "Go along with you; the flounder can give us one."

"Now, wife," said the man, "the flounder gave us the cottage; I do not like to go to him again, he may be angry."

"Go along," said the wife, "he might just as well give us it as not; do as I say!"

The man felt very reluctant and unwilling; and he said to himself,

"It is not the right thing to do"; nevertheless he went.

So when he came to the seaside, the water was purple and dark blue and grey and thick, and not green and yellow as before. And he stood and said,

"O man, O man!—if man you be,
Or flounder, flounder, in the sea—
Such a tiresome wife I've got,
For she wants what I do not."

"Now then, what does she want?" said the flounder.

"Oh," said the man, half frightened, "she wants to live in a large stone castle."

"Go home with you, she is already standing before the door," said the flounder.

Then the man went home, as he supposed, but when he got there, there stood in the place of the cottage a great castle of stone, and his wife was standing on the steps, about to go in; so she took him by the hand, and said,

"Let us enter."

With that he went in with her, and in the castle was a great hall with a marble pavement, and there were a great many servants, who led them through large doors, and the passages were decked with tapestry, and the rooms with golden chairs and tables, and crystal chandeliers hanging from the ceiling; and all the rooms had carpets. And the tables were covered with eatables and the best wine for any one who wanted them. And at the back of the house was a great stable-yard for horses and

144

cattle, and carriages of the finest; besides, there was a splendid large garden, with the most beautiful flowers and fine fruit trees, and a pleasance full half a mile long, with deer and oxen and sheep, and everything that heart could wish for.

"There!" said the wife, "is not this beautiful?"

"Oh yes," said the man, "if it will only last we can live in this fine castle and be very well contented."

"We will see about that," said the wife, "in the meanwhile we will sleep upon it." With that they went to bed.

The next morning the wife was awake first, just at the break of day, and she looked out and saw from her bed the beautiful country lying all around. The man took no notice of it, so she poked him in the side with her elbow, and said,

"Husband, get up and just look out of the window. Look, just think if we could be king over all this country. Just go to your fish and tell him we should like to be king."

"Now, wife," said the man, "what should we be kings for? I don't want to be king."

"Well," said the wife, "if you don't want to be king, I will be king."

"Now, wife," said the man, "what do you want to be king for? I could not ask him such a thing."

"Why not?" said the wife. "You must go directly all the same; I must be king."

So the man went, very much put out that his wife should want to be king.

"It is not the right thing to do—not at all the right thing," thought the man. He did not at all want to go, and yet he went all the same.

145

And when he came to the sea the water was quite dark grey, and rushed far inland, and had an ill smell. And he stood and said,

"O man, O man!—if man you be,
  Or flounder, flounder, in the sea—
Such a tiresome wife I've got,
For she wants what I do not."

"Now then, what does she want?" said the fish.

"Oh dear!" said the man. "She wants to be king."

"Go home with you, she is so already," said the fish.

So the man went back, and as he came to the palace he saw it was very much larger, and had great towers and splendid gate-ways; the herald stood before the door, and a number of soldiers with kettle-drums and trumpets.

And when he came inside everything was of marble and gold, and there were many curtains with great golden tassels. Then he went through the doors of the saloon to where the great throne-room was, and there was his wife sitting upon a throne of gold and diamonds, and she had a great golden crown on, and the sceptre in her hand was of pure gold and jewels, and on each side stood six pages in a row, each one a head shorter than the other. So the man went up to her and said,

"Well, wife, so now you are king!"

"Yes," said the wife, "now I am king."

So then he stood and looked at her, and when he had gazed at her for some time he said,

"Well, wife, this is fine for you to be king! Now there is nothing more to wish for."

"O husband!" said the wife, seeming quite restless, "I am tired of this already. Go to your fish and tell him that now I am king I must be emperor."

"Now, wife," said the man, "what do you want to be emperor for?"

"Husband," said she, "go and tell the fish I want to be emperor."

"Oh dear!" said the man. "He could not do it—I cannot ask him such a thing. There is but one emperor at a time; the fish can't possibly make any one emperor—indeed he can't."

"Now, look here," said the wife, "I am king, and you are only my husband, so will you go at once? Go along! For if he was able to make me king he is able to make me emperor; and I will and must be emperor, so go along!"

So he was obliged to go; and as he went he felt very uncomfortable about it, and he thought to himself,

"It is not at all the right thing to do; to want to be emperor is really going too far; the flounder will soon be beginning to get tired of this."

With that he came to the sea, and the water was quite black and thick, and the foam flew, and the wind blew, and the man was terrified. But he stood and said,

"O man, O man!—if man you be,
  Or flounder, flounder, in the sea—
  Such a tiresome wife I've got,
  For she wants what I do not."

"What is it now?" said the fish.

"Oh dear!" said the man. "My wife wants to be emperor."

147

"Go home with you," said the fish, "she is emperor already."

So the man went home, and found the castle adorned with polished marble and alabaster figures, and golden gates. The troops were being marshalled before the door, and they were blowing trumpets and beating drums and cymbals; and when he entered he saw barons and earls and dukes waiting about like servants; and the doors were of bright gold. And he saw his wife sitting upon a throne made of one entire piece of gold, and it was about two miles high; and she had a great golden crown on, which was about three yards high, set with brilliants and carbuncles; and in one hand she held the sceptre, and in the other the globe; and on both sides of her stood pages in two rows, all arranged according to their size, from the most enormous giant of two miles high to the tiniest dwarf of the size of my little finger; and before her stood earls and dukes in crowds. So the man went up to her and said,

"Well, wife, so now you are emperor."

"Yes," said she, "now I am emperor."

Then he went and sat down and had a good look at her, and then he said,

"Well now, wife, there is nothing left to be, now you are emperor."

"What are you talking about, husband?" said she. "I am emperor, and next I will be pope! So go and tell the fish so."

"Oh dear!" said the man, "what is it that you don't want? You can never become pope; there is but one pope in Christendom, and the fish can't possibly do it."

"Husband," said she, "no more words about it. I must and will be pope; so go along to the fish."

"Now, wife," said the man, "how can I ask him such a thing? It is too bad—it is asking a little too much; and, besides, he could not do it."

"What rubbish!" said the wife. "If he could make me emperor he can make me pope. Go along and ask him; I am emperor, and you are only my husband, so go you must."

So he went, feeling very frightened, and he shivered and shook, and his knees trembled; and there arose a great wind, and the clouds flew by, and it grew very dark, and the sea rose mountains high, and the ships were tossed about, and the sky was partly blue in the middle, but at the sides very dark and red, as in a great tempest. And he felt very desponding, and stood trembling and said,

"O man, O man!—if man you be,
 Or flounder, flounder, in the sea—
 Such a tiresome wife I've got,
 For she wants what I do not."

"Well, what now?" said the fish.
"Oh dear!" said the man. "She wants to be pope."
"Go home with you, she is pope already," said the fish.

So he went home, and he found himself before a great church, with palaces all round. He had to make his way through a crowd of people; and when he got inside he found the place lighted up with thousands and thousands of lights; and his wife was clothed in a golden garment, and sat upon a very high throne, and had three golden crowns on, all in the greatest priestly pomp; and on both sides of her there stood two rows of lights of all sizes—from the size of the longest tower to the smallest rushlight, and all the emperors and kings were kneeling before her and kissing her foot.

"Well, wife," said the man, and sat and stared at her, "so you are pope."

"Yes," said she, "now I am pope!"

And he went on gazing at her till he felt dazzled, as if he were sitting in the sun. And after a little time he said,

"Well, now, wife, what is there left to be, now you are pope?" And she sat up very stiff and straight, and said nothing.

And he said again, "Well, wife, I hope you are contented at last with being pope; you can be nothing more."

"We will see about that," said the wife. With that they both went to bed; but she was as far as ever from being contented, and she could not get to sleep for thinking of what she should like to be next.

The husband, however, slept as fast as a top after his busy day; but the wife tossed and turned from side to side the whole night through, thinking all the while what she could be next, but nothing would occur to her; and when she saw the red dawn she slipped off the bed, and sat before the window to see the sun rise, and as it came up she said,

"Ah, I have it! What if I should make the sun and moon to rise—husband!" she cried, and stuck her elbow in his ribs. "Wake up, and go to your fish, and tell him I want power over the sun and moon."

The man was so fast asleep that when he started up he fell out of bed. Then he shook himself together, and opened his eyes and said,

"Oh—wife, what did you say?"

"Husband," said she, "if I cannot get the power of making the sun and moon rise when I want them, I shall never have another quiet hour. Go to the fish and tell him so."

"O wife!" said the man, and fell on his knees to her. "The fish can really not do that for you. I grant you he could make you emperor and pope; do be contented with that, I beg of you."

And she became wild with impatience, and screamed out, "I can wait no longer, go at once!"

And so off he went as well as he could for fright. And a dreadful storm arose, so that he could hardly keep his feet; and the houses and trees were blown down, and the mountains trembled, and rocks fell in the sca; the sky was quite black, and it thundered and lightened; and the waves, crowned with foam, ran mountains high. So he cried out, without being able to hear his own words,

"O man, O man!—if man you be,
Or flounder, flounder, in the sea—
Such a tiresome wife I've got,
For she wants what I do not."

"Well, what now?" said the flounder.

"Oh dear!" said the man. "She wants to order about the sun and moon."

"Go home with you!" said the flounder. "You will find her in the old hovel."

And there they are sitting to this very day.

# The Gallant Tailor

One summer morning a little tailor was sitting on his board near the window, and working cheerfully with all his might, when an old woman came down the street crying,

"Good jelly to sell! Good jelly to sell!"

The cry sounded pleasant in the little tailor's ears, so he put his head out of the window, and called out,

"Here, my good woman—come here, if you want a customer."

So the poor woman climbed the steps with her heavy basket, and was obliged to unpack and display all her pots to the tailor. He looked at every one of them, and lifting all the lids, applied his nose to each, and said at last,

"The jelly seems pretty good; you may weigh me out four half ounces, or I don't mind having a quarter of a pound."

The woman, who had expected to find a good customer, gave

him what he asked for, but went off angry and grumbling.

"This jelly is the very thing for me," cried the little tailor; "it will give me strength and cunning"; and he took down the bread from the cupboard, cut a whole round of the loaf, and spread the jelly on it, laid it near him, and went on stitching more gallantly than ever. All the while the scent of the sweet jelly was spreading throughout the room, where there were quantities of flies, who were attracted by it and flew to partake.

"Now then, who asked you to come?" said the tailor, and drove the unbidden guests away. But the flies, not understanding his language, were not to be got rid of like that, and returned in larger numbers than before. Then the tailor, not being able to stand it any longer, took from his chimney-corner a ragged cloth, and saying,

"Now, I'll let you have it!" beat it among them unmercifully. When he ceased, and counted the slain, he found seven lying dead before him.

"This is indeed somewhat," he said, wondering at his own gallantry. "The whole town shall know this." ·

So he hastened to cut out a belt, and he stitched it, and put on it in large capitals "Seven at one blow!"

"—The town, did I say!" said the little tailor. "The whole world shall know it!" And his heart quivered with joy, like a lamb's tail.

The tailor fastened the belt round him, and began to think of going out into the world, for his workshop seemed too small for his worship. So he looked about in all the house for something that it would be useful to take with him, but he found nothing but an old cheese, which he put in his pocket. Outside the door he noticed that a bird had got caught in the bushes, so he took that and put it in his pocket with the cheese. Then he set out gallantly on his way, and as he was light and active he felt no fatigue. The way led over a mountain, and when he reached the topmost peak he saw a terrible giant sitting there, and looking about him at his ease. The tailor went bravely up to him, called out to him, and said,

"Comrade, good day! There you sit looking over the wide world! I am on the way thither to seek my fortune: have you a fancy to go with me?"

The giant looked at the tailor contemptuously, and said, "You little rascal! You miserable fellow!"

"That may be!" answered the little tailor, and undoing his coat he showed the giant his belt. "You can read there whether I am a man or not!"

The giant read: "Seven at one blow!" and thinking it meant men that the tailor had killed, felt at once more respect for the little fellow. But as he wanted to prove him, he took up a stone and squeezed it so hard that water came out of it.

"Now you can do that," said the giant, "that is, if you have the strength for it."

"That's not much," said the little tailor, "I call that play," and he put his hand in his pocket and took out the cheese and squeezed it, so that the whey ran out of it.

"Well," said he, "what do you think of that?"

The giant did not know what to say to it, for he could not have believed it of the little man. Then the giant took up a stone and threw it so high that it was nearly out of sight.

"Now, little fellow, suppose you do that!"

"Well thrown," said the tailor; "but the stone fell back to earth again—I will throw you one that will never come back." So he felt in his pocket, took out the bird, and threw it into the air. And the bird, when it found itself at liberty, took wing, flew off, and returned no more.

"What do you think of that, comrade?" asked the tailor.

"There is no doubt that you throw," said the giant; "but we will see if you can carry."

He led the little tailor to a mighty oak-tree which had been felled, and was lying on the ground, and said,

"Now, if you are strong enough, help me to carry this tree out of the wood."

"Willingly," answered the little man; "you take the trunk on your shoulders, I will take the branches with all their foliage, that is much the most difficult."

So the giant took the trunk on his shoulders, and the tailor seated himself on a branch, and the giant, who could not see what he was doing, had the whole tree to carry, and the little man on it as well. And the little man was very cheerful and merry, and whistled the tune: *"There were three tailors riding by,"* as if carrying the tree was mere child's play. The giant, when he had struggled on under his heavy load a part of the way, was tired out, and cried,

"Look here, I must let go the tree!"

The tailor jumped off quickly, and taking hold of the tree with both arms, as if he were carrying it, said to the giant,

"You see you can't carry the tree though you are such a big fellow!"

They went on together a little farther, and presently they

came to a cherry-tree, and the giant took hold of the topmost branches, where the ripest fruit hung, and pulling them downwards, gave them to the tailor to hold, bidding him eat. But the little tailor was much too weak to hold the tree, and as the giant let go, the tree sprang back, and the tailor was caught up into the air. And when he dropped down again without any damage, the giant said to him,

"How is this? Haven't you strength enough to hold such a weak sprig as that?"

"It is not strength that is lacking," answered the little tailor. "How should it be to one who has slain seven at one blow! I just jumped over the tree because the hunters are shooting down there in the bushes. You jump it too, if you can."

The giant made the attempt, and not being able to vault the tree, he remained hanging in the branches, so that once more the little tailor got the better of him. Then said the giant,

"As you are such a gallant fellow, suppose you come with me to our den, and stay the night."

The tailor was quite willing, and he followed him. When they reached the den there sat some other giants by the fire, and each had a roasted sheep in his hand, and was eating it. The little tailor looked round and thought,

"There is more elbow-room here than in my workshop."

And the giant showed him a bed, and told him he had better lie down upon it and go to sleep. The bed was, however, too big for the tailor, so he did not stay in it, but crept into a corner to sleep. As soon as it was midnight the giant got up, took a great staff of iron and beat the bed through with one stroke, and supposed he had made an end of that grasshopper of a tailor.

Very early in the morning the giants went into the wood and forgot all about the little tailor, and when they saw him coming after them alive and merry, they were terribly frightened, and, thinking he was going to kill them, they ran away in all haste.

So the little tailor marched on, always following his nose. And after he had gone a great way he entered the courtyard belonging to a King's palace, and there he felt so overpowered with fatigue that he lay down and fell asleep. In the meanwhile came various people, who looked at him very curiously, and read on his belt, "Seven at one blow!"

"Oh!" said they, "why should this great lord come here in time of peace? What a mighty champion he must be!"

Then they went and told the King about him, and they thought that if war should break out what a worthy and useful man he would be, and that he ought not to be allowed to depart at any price. The King then summoned his council, and sent one of his courtiers to the little tailor to beg him, so soon as he should wake up, to consent to serve in the King's army. So the messenger stood and waited at the sleeper's side until his limbs began to stretch, and his eyes to open, and then he carried his answer back. And the answer was,

"That was the reason for which I came," said the little tailor, "I am ready to enter the King's service."

So he was received into it very honourably, and a separate dwelling set apart for him.

But the rest of the soldiers were very much set against the little tailor, and they wished him a thousand miles away.

"What shall be done about it?" they said among them-

158

selves; "if we pick a quarrel and fight with him then seven of us will fall at each blow. That will be of no good to us."

So they came to a resolution, and went all together to the King to ask for their discharge.

"We never intended," said they, "to serve with a man who kills seven at a blow."

The King felt sorry to lose all his faithful servants because of one man, and he wished that he had never seen him, and would willingly get rid of him if he might. But he did not dare to dismiss the little tailor for fear he should kill all the King's people, and place himself upon the throne. He thought a long while about it, and at last made up his mind what to do. He sent for the little tailor, and told him that he was so great a warrior he had a proposal to make to him. He told him that in a wood in his dominions dwelt two giants, who did great damage by robbery, murder, and fire, and that no man durst go near them for fear of his life. But that if the tailor should overcome and slay both these giants the King would give him his only daughter in marriage, and half his kingdom as dowry, and that a hundred horsemen should go with him to give him assistance.

"That would be something for a man like me!" thought the little tailor. "A beautiful princess and half a kingdom are not to be had every day." And he said to the King,

"Oh yes, I can soon overcome the giants, and yet have no need of the hundred horsemen; he who can kill seven at one blow has no need to be afraid of two."

So the little tailor set out, and the hundred horsemen followed him. When he came to the border of the wood he said to his escort,

"Stay here while I go to attack the giants."

Then he sprang into the wood, and looked about him right and left. After a while he caught sight of the two giants; they were lying down under a tree asleep, and snoring so that all the branches shook. The little tailor, all alive, filled both his pockets with stones and climbed up into the tree, and made his way to an overhanging bough, so that he could seat himself just above the sleepers; and from there he let one stone after another fall on the chest of one of the giants. For a long time the giant was quite unaware of this, but at last he waked up and pushed his comrade, and said,

"What are you hitting me for?"

"You are dreaming," said the other, "I am not touching you." And they composed themselves again to sleep, and the tailor let fall a stone on the other giant.

"What can that be?" cried he. "What are you casting at me?"

"I am casting nothing at you," answered the first, grumbling.

They disputed about it for a while, but as they were tired, they gave it up at last, and their eyes closed once more. Then the little tailor began his game anew, picked out a heavier stone and threw it down with force upon the first giant's chest.

"This is too much!" cried he, and sprang up like a madman and struck his companion such a blow that the tree shook above them. The other paid him back with ready coin, and they fought with such fury that they tore up trees by their roots to use for weapons against each other, so that at last they both of them lay dead upon the ground. And now the little tailor got down.

"Another piece of luck!" said he, "that the tree I was sitting in did not get torn up too, or else I should have had to jump like a squirrel from one tree to another."

Then he drew his sword and gave each of the giants a few hacks in the breast, and went back to the horsemen and said,

"The deed is done, I have made an end of both of them: but it went hard with me, in the struggle they rooted up trees to defend themselves, but it was of no use, they had to do with a man who can kill seven at one blow."

"Then are you not wounded?" asked the horsemen.

"Nothing of the sort!" answered the tailor. "I have not turned a hair."

The horsemen still would not believe it and rode into the wood to see, and there they found the giants wallowing in their blood, and all about them lying the uprooted trees.

The little tailor then claimed the promised boon, but the King repented him of his offer, and he sought again how to rid himself of the hero.

"Before you can possess my daughter and the half of my kingdom," said he to the tailor, "you must perform another heroic act. In the wood lives a unicorn who does great damage; you must secure him."

"A unicorn does not strike more terror into me than two giants. Seven at one blow—that is my way!" was the tailor's answer.

So, taking a rope and an axe with him, he went out into the wood, and told those who were ordered to attend him to wait outside. He had not far to seek, the unicorn soon came out and sprang at him, as if he would make an end of him without delay. "Softly, softly," said he, "most haste, worst speed," and remained standing until the animal came quite near, then he slipped quietly behind a tree. The unicorn ran with all his might against the tree and stuck his horn so deep into the trunk that he could not get it out again, and so was taken.

"Now I have you," said the tailor, coming out from behind the tree, and, putting the rope around the unicorn's neck, he took the axe, set free the horn, and when all his party were assembled he led forth the animal and brought it to the King.

The King did not yet wish to give him the promised reward, and set him a third task to do. Before the wedding could take place the tailor was to secure a wild boar which had done a great deal of damage in the wood.

The huntsmen were to accompany him.

"All right," said the tailor, "this is child's play."

But he did not take the huntsmen into the wood, and they were all the better pleased, for the wild boar had many a time before received them in such a way that they had no fancy to disturb him. When the boar caught sight of the tailor he ran at him with foaming mouth and gleaming tusks to bear him to the ground, but the nimble hero rushed into a chapel which chanced to be near, and jumped quickly out of a window on the other side. The boar ran after him, and when he got inside the door shut after him, and there he was imprisoned, for the creature was too big and unwieldy to jump out of the window too. Then the little tailor called the huntsmen that they might see the prisoner with their own eyes; and then he betook himself to the king, who now, whether he liked it or not, was obliged to fulfil his promise, and gave him his daughter and half of his kingdom. But if he had known that the great warrior was only a little tailor he would have taken it still more to heart. So the wedding was celebrated with great splendour and little joy, and the tailor was made into a king.

One night the young queen heard her husband talking in his sleep and saying,

"Now boy, make me that waistcoat and patch me those breeches, or I will lay my yard measure about your shoulders!"

And so, as she perceived of what low birth her husband was, she went to her father the next morning and told him all, and begged him to set her free from a man who was nothing better than a tailor. The king bade her be comforted, saying,

"To-night leave your bedroom door open, my guard shall stand outside, and when he is asleep they shall come in and bind him and carry him off to a ship, and he shall be sent to the other side of the world."

So the wife felt consoled, but the king's water-bearer, who had been listening all the while, went to the little tailor and disclosed to him the whole plan.

"I shall put a stop to all this," said he.

At night he lay down as usual in bed, and when his wife thought that he was asleep, she got up, opened the door and lay down again. The little tailor, who only made believe to be asleep, began to murmur plainly,

"Now, boy, make me that waistcoat and patch me those breeches, or I will lay my yard measure about your shoulders!

I have slain seven at one blow, killed two giants, caught a unicorn, and taken a wild boar, and shall I be afraid of those who are standing outside my room door?"

And when they heard the tailor say this, a great fear seized them; they fled away as if they had been wild hares, and none of them would venture to attack him.

And so the little tailor all his lifetime remained a king.

# Aschenputtel

There was once a rich man whose wife lay sick, and when she felt her end drawing near she called to her only daughter to come near her bed, and said,

"Dear child, be pious and good, and God will always take care of you, and I will look down upon you from heaven, and will be with you."

And then she closed her eyes and expired. The maiden went every day to her mother's grave and wept, and was always pious and good. When the winter came the snow covered the grave with a white covering, and when the sun came in the early spring and melted it away, the man took to himself another wife.

The new wife brought two daughters home with her, and they were beautiful and fair in appearance, but at heart were black and ugly. And then began very evil times for the poor step-daughter.

"Is the stupid creature to sit in the same room with us?" said they. "Those who eat food must earn it. Out upon her for a kitchen-maid!"

They took away her pretty dresses and put on her an old grey kirtle, and gave her wooden shoes to wear.

"Just look now at the proud princess, how she is decked out!" cried they laughing, and then they sent her into the kitchen. There she was obliged to do heavy work from morning to night, get up early in the morning, draw water, make the fires, cook, and wash. Besides that, the sisters did their utmost to torment her—mocking her, and strewing peas and lentils among the ashes, and setting her to pick them up. In the evenings, when she was quite tired out with her hard day's work, she had no bed to lie on, but was obliged to rest on the hearth among the cinders. And as she always looked dusty and dirty, they named her Aschenputtel.

It happened one day that the father went to the fair, and he asked his two step-daughters what he should bring back for them.

"Fine clothes!" said one.

"Pearls and jewels!" said the other.

"But what will you have, Aschenputtel?" said he.

"The first twig, father, that strikes against your hat on the way home; that is what I should like you to bring me."

So he bought for the two step-daughters fine clothes, pearls, and jewels, and on his way back, as he rode through a green lane, a hazel-twig struck against his hat; and he broke it off and carried it home with him. And when he reached home he gave to the step-daughters what they had wished for, and to Aschenputtel he gave the hazel-twig. She thanked him, and went to her mother's grave, and planted this twig there, weeping so bitterly that the tears fell upon it and watered it, and it flourished and became a fine tree. Aschenputtel went to see it three times a day, and wept and prayed, and each time a white bird rose up from the tree, and if she uttered any wish the bird brought her whatever she had wished for.

Now it came to pass that the king ordained a festival that should last for three days, and to which all the beautiful young women of that country were bidden, so that the king's son might choose a bride from among them. When the two step-daughters heard that they too were bidden to appear, they felt very pleased, and they called Aschenputtel, and said,

"Comb our hair, brush our shoes, and make our buckles fast, we are going to the wedding feast at the king's castle."

Aschenputtel, when she heard this, could not help crying, for she too would have liked to go to the dance, and she begged her step-mother to allow her.

"What, you, Aschenputtel!" said she. "In all your dust and dirt, you want to go to the festival! You that have no dress and no shoes! You want to dance!"

But as she persisted in asking, at last the step-mother said,

"I have strewed a dish full of lentils in the ashes, and if you can pick them all up again in two hours you may go with us."

Then the maiden went to the back-door that led into the garden, and called out,

167

"O gentle doves, O turtle-doves,
 And all the birds that be,
 The lentils that in ashes lie
 Come and pick up for me!
   The good must be put in the dish,
   The bad you may eat if you wish."

Then there came to the kitchen-window two white doves,
and after them some turtle-doves, and at last a crowd of all
the birds under heaven, chirping and fluttering, and they
alighted among the ashes; and the doves nodded with their
heads, and began to pick, peck, pick, peck, and then all the
others began to pick, peck, pick, peck, and put all the good
grains into the dish. Before an hour was over all was done,
and they flew away. Then the maiden brought the dish to her
step-mother, feeling joyful, and thinking that now she should
go to the feast; but the step-mother said,

"No, Aschenputtel, you have no proper clothes, and you do
not know how to dance, and you would be laughed at!"

And when Aschenputtel cried for disappointment, she
added,

"If you can pick two dishes full of lentils out of the ashes,
nice and clean, you shall go with us," thinking to herself, "for
that is not possible." When she had strewed two dishes full
of lentils among the ashes the maiden went through the back-
door into the garden, and cried,

"O gentle doves, O turtle-doves,
 And all the birds that be,
 The lentils that in ashes lie

Come and pick up for me!
  The good must be put in the dish,
  The bad you may eat if you wish."

So there came to the kitchen-window two white doves, and then some turtle-doves, and at last a crowd of all the other birds under heaven, chirping and fluttering, and they alighted among the ashes, and the doves nodded with their heads and began to pick, peck, pick, peck, and then all the others began to pick, peck, pick, peck, and put all the good grains into the dish. And before half-an-hour was over it was all done, and they flew away. Then the maiden took the dishes to the step-mother, feeling joyful, and thinking that now she should go with them to the feast; but she said, "All this is of no good to you; you cannot come with us, for you have no proper clothes, and cannot dance; you would put us to shame."

Then she turned her back on poor Aschenputtel, and made haste to set out with her two proud daughters.

And as there was no one left in the house, Aschenputtel went to her mother's grave, under the hazel bush, and cried,

"Little tree, little tree, shake over me,
That silver and gold may come down and cover me."

Then the bird threw down a dress of gold and silver, and a pair of slippers embroidered with silk and silver. And in all haste she put on the dress and went to the festival. But her step-mother and sisters did not know her, and thought she must be a foreign princess, she looked so beautiful in her golden dress. Of Aschenputtel they never thought at all, and supposed that she was sitting at home, and picking the lentils out of the ashes. The King's son came to meet her, and took her by the hand and danced with her, and he refused to stand up with any one else, so that he might not be obliged to let go her hand; and when any one came to claim it he answered, "She is my partner."

And when the evening came she wanted to go home, but the prince said he would go with her to take care of her, for he wanted to see where the beautiful maiden lived. But she escaped him, and jumped up into the pigeon-house. Then the prince waited until the father came, and told him the strange maiden had jumped into the pigeon-house. The father thought to himself,

"It cannot surely be Aschenputtel," and called for axes and hatchets, and had the pigeon-house cut down, but there was no one in it. And when they entered the house there sat Aschenputtel in her dirty clothes among the cinders, and a little oil-lamp burnt dimly in the chimney; for Aschenputtel had been very quick, and had jumped out of the pigeon-house again, and had run to the hazel bush; and there she had taken off her beautiful dress and had laid it on the grave, and the bird had carried it away again, and then she had put on her little grey kirtle again, and had sat down in the kitchen among the cinders.

The next day, when the festival began anew, and the parents and step-sisters had gone to it, Aschenputtel went to the hazel bush and cried,

"Little tree, little tree, shake over me,
 That silver and gold may come down and cover me."

Then the bird cast down a still more splendid dress than on

170

the day before. And when she appeared in it among the guests every one was astonished at her beauty. The prince had been waiting until she came, and he took her hand and danced with her alone. And when any one else came to invite her he said, "She is my partner."

And when the evening came she wanted to go home, and the prince followed her, for he wanted to see to what house she belonged; but she broke away from him, and ran into the garden at the back of the house. There stood a fine large tree, bearing splendid pears; she leapt as lightly as a squirrel among the branches, and the prince did not know what had become of her. So he waited until the father came, and then he told him that the strange maiden had rushed from him, and that he thought she had gone up into the pear-tree. The father thought to himself,

"It cannot surely be Aschenputtel," and called for an axe, and felled the tree, but there was no one in it. And when they went into the kitchen there sat Aschenputtel among the cinders, as usual, for she had got down the other side of the tree, and had taken back her beautiful clothes to the bird on the hazel bush, and had put on her old grey kirtle again.

On the third day, when the parents and the step-children had set off, Aschenputtel went again to her mother's grave, and said to the tree,

"Little tree, little tree, shake over me,
 That silver and gold may come down and cover me."

Then the bird cast down a dress, the like of which had never been seen for splendour and brilliancy, and slippers that were of gold.

And when she appeared in this dress at the feast nobody knew what to say for wonderment. The prince danced with her alone, and if any one else asked her he answered,

"She is my partner."

And when it was evening Aschenputtel wanted to go home, and the prince was about to go with her, when she ran past him so quickly that he could not follow her. But he had laid a plan, and had caused all the steps to be spread with pitch, so that as she rushed down them the left shoe of the maiden remained sticking in it. The prince picked it up, and saw that it was of gold, and very small and slender. The next morning he went to the father and told him that none should be his bride save the one whose foot the golden shoe should fit. Then the two sisters were very glad, because they had pretty feet. The eldest went to her room to try on the shoe, and her mother stood by. But she could not get her great toe into it, for the shoe was too small; then her mother handed her a knife, and said,

"Cut the toe off, for when you are queen you will never have to go on foot." So the girl cut her toe off, squeezed her foot into the shoe, concealed the pain, and went down to the prince. Then he took her with him on his horse as his bride, and rode off. They had to pass by the grave, and there sat the two pigeons on the hazel bush, and cried,

"There they go, there they go!
 There is blood on her shoe;
 The shoe is too small,
 —Not the right bride at all!"

Then the prince looked at her shoe, and saw the blood

flowing. And he turned his horse round and took the false bride home again, saying she was not the right one, and that the other sister must try on the shoe. So she went into her room to do so, and got her toes comfortably in, but her heel was too large. Then her mother handed her the knife, saying, "Cut a piece off your heel; when you are queen you will never have to go on foot."

So the girl cut a piece off her heel, and thrust her foot into the shoe, concealed the pain, and went down to the prince, who took his bride before him on his horse and rode off. When they passed by the hazel bush the two pigeons sat there and cried,

"There they go, there they go!
There is blood on her shoe;
The shoe is too small,
—Not the right bride at all!"

Then the prince looked at her foot, and saw how the blood was flowing from the shoe, and staining the white stocking. And he turned his horse round and brought the false bride home again.

"This is not the right one," said he, "have you no other daughter?"

"No," said the man, "only my dead wife left behind her a little stunted Aschenputtel; it is impossible that she can be the bride." But the King's son ordered her to be sent for, but the mother said,

"Oh no! She is much too dirty, I could not let her be seen."

But he would have her fetched, and so Aschenputtel had to appear.

First she washed her face and hands quite clean, and went in and curtseyed to the prince, who held out to her the golden shoe. Then she sat down on a stool, drew her foot out of the heavy wooden shoe, and slipped it into the golden one, which fitted it perfectly. And when she stood up, and the prince looked in her face, he knew again the beautiful maiden that had danced with him, and he cried,

"This is the right bride!"

The step-mother and the two sisters were thunderstruck, and grew pale with anger; but he put Aschenputtel before him on his horse and rode off. And as they passed the hazel bush, the two white pigeons cried,

"There they go, there they go!
 No blood on her shoe;
 The shoe's not too small,
 The right bride is she after all."

And when they had thus cried, they came flying after and perched on Aschenputtel's shoulders, one on the right, the other on the left, and so remained.

And when her wedding with the prince was appointed to be held the false sisters came, hoping to curry favour, and to take part in the festivities. So as the bridal procession went to the church, the elder walked on the right side and the younger on the left, and the pigeons picked out an eye of each of them. And as they returned the elder was on the left side and the younger on the right, and the pigeons picked out the other eye of each of them. And so they were condemned to go blind for the rest of their days because of their wickedness and falsehood.

Abbey